To: Syd & Mimi Bush

It's good to make new
Friends — Hope you
enjoy the Book —

Best Wishes —

[signature]

13 Dec 86

AMERICA'S ASTRONAUTS
AND THEIR
INDESTRUCTIBLE
SPIRIT

This book is dedicated to those who gave their lives
in the exploration of space, and to Danny.

AMERICA'S ASTRONAUTS
AND THEIR
INDESTRUCTIBLE
SPIRIT

DR. FRED KELLY, FORMER NASA PHYSICIAN
FOREWORD BY DR. BUZZ ALDRIN

AERO
A division of TAB BOOKS Inc.
Blue Ridge Summit, PA 17214

FIRST EDITION

FIRST PRINTING

Library of Congress Cataloging in Publication Data

Kelly, Fred, 1926-
    America's Astronauts and Their Indestructible Spirit.

    Includes index.
    1. Astronautics—United States. 2. Space medicine.
I. Title.
TL789.8.U5K39   1986   629.4'0973   86-5890
ISBN 0-8306-8396-8

Cover photograph courtesy of NASA.

Contents

Foreword

Shortly after being selected as a NASA astronaut, I met Fred Kelly. He was my neighbor, my friend, and my flight surgeon for over four years. Although I knew of his skills as a naval aviator and a physician, until reading this manuscript I did not know of his superb story-telling abilities. In *INDESTRUCTIBLE*, he offers the reader an authentic history of the human side of man's spaceflight that reads like a novel.

We who were chosen to fly in space approached each mission with a confidence that anything short of success was unthinkable. We were aware that risk was inherent in our task, and the possibility of disaster was ever present. However, accidents always happen to someone else. We never believed we were doing anything extraordinarily dangerous. We were doing our job. We were working within our sphere of experience and expertise and, therefore, were confident in our ability to do the job for which we were exceedingly well trained.

The job consumed us. It consumed our families. Those closest to us were either swept up in the obsession as completely as we were, or they were swept aside. In this book, Dr. Kelly tells of the hidden costs to those involved in the early manned Space program. *INDESTRUCTIBLE* is a story that was waiting to be told.

Dr. Buzz Aldrin

Acknowledgments

It is impossible to acknowledge each of those who made this book a reality; but I couldn't rest unless I tried. James Michener because of his too-busy schedule, inadvertently launched me on this project. His encouragement made me continue. Professor Loraine Webster, Ph.D. labored tirelessly over the first draft and gave me valuable professional guidance. Her son-in-law, my son, Dewey Kelly, in addition to living this story, added his editorial talents. Dr. Paul Buchanan, director of the Biomedical Office at Kennedy Space Center, finally persuaded me to lay aside personal modesty and to share this experience in first person. He and other NASA friends arranged for the many excellent illustrations in this volume. Chris Carey of Aeolus Ltd. encouraged me to rekindle my interest in this project and prepare it for publication. Ray Collins of TAB BOOKS rewarded my renewed effort by accepting the manuscript for publication. Jimi and Diane Kelly, as wife and daughter, saw me through the living and the writing of this story.

To them and to the multitude of others who shared this experience and gave me their unbridled advice, criticism, and encouragement, I offer my humble thanks.

Introduction

The belief in indestructibility is as old as the human spirit; on this belief depends our very survival. We have known it by many names, but someone in each era has had a vision of a completed goal and the confidence that this goal could be achieved. We have survived! We need no other proof of our indestructibility.

Take our accomplishments: truly great accomplishments have never been given to those without vision—without confidence. The men and women in this story had vision—they had confidence. Their accomplishments are history.

This is a story of the early United States space program and of the men who believed they were indestructible. The characters and events in the story are real. Historical facts are not distorted. Many of the conversations occurred essentially as described; others were staged to emphasize important facets of the story that otherwise might have been missed.

America's Astronauts and Their Indestructible Spirit is, therefore, a factual account of the early United States space explorations related by one who was fortunate to have been personally involved in each of this nation's manned space programs from Project Mercury to the Space Shuttle Program (officially known as the Space Transportation System). It is a personal view of the space program; it concentrates on the interpersonal relationships and sacrifices of those individuals who made space exploration possible. No previous account has addressed the cost of an astronaut's ambitions to himself, to his wife and family, and to the others who are not usually considered newsworthy. This book explores another side of the space story.

INDESTRUCTIBLE is also an introduction to the relatively unheralded medical specialty of aerospace medicine. It is not an attempt to write a historical account of aerospace medicine nor an attempt to document the notable accomplishments that so many have made in this new field of medicine. Many pioneers who contributed greatly to the success of early manned space exploration are not mentioned. For that I must offer my sincere apologies. To others, who might consider this account unduly influenced by my personal bias, I make no apologies. It is a personal story—a story based on my involvement through an exciting phase of our history. I encourage you, the reader, to experience and appreciate the excitement of this young medical specialty through the eyes of one who just happened to be there.

Some readers will possibly be unaware that such a specialty as aerospace medicine exists. Few will know that physicians were among the first to become interested in flight. Fewer still will know that the first successful manned flight was made by a physician, Pilatre de Rosier, in 1783, or that the first successful flight over the English Channel, also in a hot air balloon, was made and financed by a physician, John Jeffries, in 1785. Even though this medical specialty would not be formally recognized until nearly 170 years later, it was significant that the first flight crew to lose their lives in an aviation accident included a physician, Pilatre de Rosier, in 1785.

When James Michener was involved in research for his book *Space*, I tried to interest him in making one of his characters a flight surgeon. I wanted to give aerospace medicine the credibility he had given naval aviation in *Bridges at Toko-ri*. Someone with the literary stature and the command of the English language of a Michener could weave this small facet of space exploration into his larger story and build a classic. Although he was interested in my proposal and planned a follow-up meeting, his schedule did not allow him to explore the idea further. Michener's schedule, along with his encouragement, explains my present excursion into the field of literature.

At the outset, I had no intention of writing a book. My most ambitious goals were to occupy time between professional pursuits and to record some ideas that had been germinating for the last forty years. I have achieved my goals. I can only hope that some of you will find this offering entertaining and perhaps informative about a facet of the space program that has not attained public attention. Perhaps the next time you hear that a physician has been chosen to fly on a space shuttle mission, a glimmer of recognition will pass through your consciousness, and you will know that he or she represents a medical specialty called aerospace medicine.

| 1 |

Crash on the Flight Deck

''Wave off, four six. WAVE OFF!''

As these words echoed in my hard hat, I knew the landing signal officer's warning had come too late. The LSO had only confirmed what I had sensed seconds ago. I anticipated the wave off as soon as the meatball began to drop off the low side of the mirror. My speed brakes were coming in, throttle at 100 percent, nose rotated; I was doing my best to avoid a collision with the rapidly approaching carrier deck.

The mirror landing system had been installed about the time the old *Lady Lex* had her major face-lift. This British invention had made carrier landings much safer than they were when I first started flying Navy aircraft. The mirror landing system made it possible for the pilot to know precisely where he was in relation to the glide slope. If the *meatball*, which was a reflection of a spotlight in a curved mirror, was higher than the line of reference lights, he was above the slope. If the ball was low, he was below the glide slope.

Another British invention was the *canted deck*—the landing area of the flight deck had been set at an angle to the lon-

The U.S. Manned Space Program, from the sixties to the eighties. Clockwise from left bottom, Friendship 7 blasting off; the Gemini '76 rendezvous, Apollo 11 takes man to the moon, and the Space Shuttle Columbia. (Courtesy NASA)

1

gitudinal axis of the ship. This positioning allowed the pilot who was unlucky enough to miss the arresting gear to simply add power and retain flying speed. He had an unobstructed flight path, rather than a deck full of aircraft, as was usually the case on straight deck carriers. He had an unobstructed flight path *if* he made it over the round down and onto the carrier deck; otherwise, he went into the part of the ship that naval aviators reverently called "the spud locker." It looked very much like Spartan Four Six was about to end up in the spud locker of the U.S.S. *Lexington*.

————

Damn this gutless beast! Why didn't it jump when I added full throttle? Why didn't it have an afterburner like the F3H Demon I flew at Point Mugu? That would give me the extra thrust I needed and the bird would jump to life. Instead, the A-4C Skyhawk took several seconds to wind up to full power after the throttle was advanced. I didn't have several seconds.

The deck was now very close—and getting closer every instant. The A-4 was climbing but so was the deck. That's it! The deck was pitching. I remembered that, during the preflight briefing, we had been told that sea conditions were four to six feet. I had put this fact out of my mind because the mirror was gyro stabilized and held the same glide slope regardless of sea conditions; they would not be a significant factor in the approach. The deck, however, was not stabilized and it was moving up and down about four to six feet in each cycle. I had held the meatball dead center from the time I picked it up on the final; then when I was very close in, the ball had suddenly dropped out of sight. The timing had been exactly wrong. The deck had pitched down and I had followed it down; now the deck was pitching up. The plane and the deck would meet at the very top of the cycle. I had been suckered into a close-in-low position, and the bird didn't have enough kick to pull out of it.

————

What was a doctor doing in this position anyway? Specifically, what was Lieutenant Commander Fred Kelly, Medical Corps, U.S. Navy, doing in this position? Ma Black had asked that question. She thought her daughter had married a respectable doctor who would come back to a small Louisiana town and practice medicine. Why was this respectable doctor risking his life and her daughter's future flying jet aircraft off of

Navy aircraft carriers? Ma Black was not alone. The question had come up over and over during the last four years.

I liked to answer that question with a series of questions: Why had a naval aviator decided to go to medical school? Hadn't I built and flown model airplanes from the time I was old enough to hold a tube of glue? Hadn't I decided to be a naval aviator while I was building that magnificent model of the F4U Corsair with the inverted gull wings? Hadn't I started into flight training as soon as my age permitted me to join the Navy in 1944? Didn't I complete field carrier landing practice in the Navy's primary flight trainer at NAS Glenview in 1945?

The Yellow Peril! Now that was a real airplane—an open-cockpit biplane with plenty of power. An 18-year-old kid could do anything in a Yellow Peril. Even my hard-nosed flight instructor was impressed when I landed with a flat tire and didn't even get a wing tip, while fourteen other cadets ground-looped and dragged their wing tips on the landing mat that day because of the high and unpredictable winds off Lake Michigan.

I never told anyone that my success occurred because a foolish cadet made a low pass on a passenger train and stayed at ground level through a herd of terrified cattle in a pasture west of Chicago. I should have planned my pull up a little higher when I came to the barbed wire fence.

My major disappointment was that the aircraft carrier *Wolverine* was not available when my class was ready for carrier landing qualification. The same thing happened twelve years later when I was again ready to qualify in the T-28. I went on to advanced flight training in the F-9, again successfully field-qualifying, only to find that the training carrier was not available.

———

So here I was, qualifying on the U.S.S. *Lexington*, CVA 16, with the replacement air group in a first-line Navy attack jet. God, was I ready! By this time, I undoubtedly had more field carrier landing practice than any naval aviator in history.

I had already claimed the record of more time in flight training than any other naval aviator. I started in 1944. After twenty-six months of training, the war was over; so I dropped out to enter medical school. Later, in 1956, I had the opportunity to resume flight training and become one of the five dual-qualified naval aviator/flight surgeons on active duty at that time. During this odyssey I had accumulated forty months of Navy flight training before winning my coveted wings of gold.

Now it looked as if I might claim another record: the shortest career as a carrier pilot!

This pass had felt good from the beginning. I had made two touch-and-go landings and two previous traps. They had been a little rough, but now I felt relaxed and confident. I had caught sight of the meatball early. My airspeed, altitude, angle of attack, and the all-important meatball had been right on the money. That was a few seconds ago; now I was headed toward the spud locker.

Your whole life is supposed to flash across your consciousness when you are faced with a life-threatening condition—don't believe it! I was much too busy to review my life or even to consider any personal feelings at this time. Even before the landing signal officer's warning, I had initiated all of the actions possible to attempt a wave off: I jammed the throttle to full power, hit the speed brake switch, and pulled the stick back to raise the nose of the A-4 slightly. I realized that, by pulling the nose up, I was losing airspeed and increasing the chance of a fatal stall. I could lower the nose and regain flying speed, but if I regained flying speed and flew into the spud locker, the results would be the same.

This part of the emergency ended with a jolting, audible, *thump!* I felt the crunch of metal against metal and knew the aircraft had suffered some undetermined amount of damage. I *had* made it up on the flight deck. I *was* climbing. The A-4 finally had came to life; it was up to full power. I was really flying!

The two things that a naval aviator fears when he lands on a carrier are a ramp strike and an in-flight engagement. A *ramp strike* is when he fails to make it onto the deck and collides with the aft end of the ship. This situation usually results in ruptured fuel tanks and a large fireball. The other fear, an *in-flight engagement*, is an inadvertent engagement of the tail hook with the arresting cable while he is flying. If this happens he rapidly loses flying speed, and if the tail hook holds he is unceremoniously slammed onto the deck with resultant structural damage and danger of fire. If the tail hook does not hold, he has lost flying speed and the aircraft rolls over the side of the deck into the water.

————

On this pass I was going to experience both a ramp strike and an in-flight engagement! The A-4 was twenty feet off the deck and climbing like a scalded dog when my tail hook caught the number one wire. The tail hook had just been raked across the deck—caught between the metal of the ship and the fuselage of the aircraft. Would it hold? Probably not! Four six was apt to end this flight in the cold waters of the Atlantic Ocean.

I still did not have time to review my life or give in to any emotions I might have felt. The emergency was not over yet! The next question I had to answer was: Should I eject just as the aircraft cleared the deck? This had been a successful maneuver in a recent F-8 accident, but the A-4 did not have the same ejection seat as the F-8. The A-4 had no capability of survival from an ejection at ground level with no airspeed. The important factors were my airspeed, my attitude or nose position, my rate of descent, and my actual altitude at the time of ejection. I knew I had lost most of my airspeed; my attitude and rate of descent would determine exactly when I needed to eject; my altitude would determine whether I landed in the ocean or was intercepted by a part of the ship. There were too many variables over which I had little control!

I knew that the chances of getting out after riding an A-4 Skyhawk into the water were equally dismal. As Carrier Air Group Flight Surgeon, I had recently reviewed the last five aircraft accident reports involving A-4s that had gone into the waters off aircraft carriers. The medical officer's reports were brief on four of these because there were no survivors.

The fifth report told a fascinating horror story of an experienced squadron commander who pulled the ejection curtain under water with no results. The ejection sequence is tied by a lanyard to the canopy release, and the canopy was held closed by water pressure; therefore, the seat would not fire. All of this time the pilot was going down, inverted, in the dark Atlantic waters. After releasing himself manually from the seat, he was able to break the canopy with his survival knife. By this time he was more than twenty feet under water, fighting for air, and tangled in a deployed parachute. With superhuman effort, this experienced pilot was able to survive and give the flight surgeon valuable information and suggestions on how to improve the ejection and escape system. This situation had occurred less than two months ago, and the changes had not been implemented yet.

––––––––––

The second contact with the deck was surprisingly soft. My landing gear was breaking away, and the external fuel tanks were taking much of the impact. The tail hook had held its grip on the number one arresting cable, and what was left of the A-4 was brought to an abrupt, but smooth, halt. I had still not made the decision to eject or ride it in, and now, thank

God, I did not have to make that decision.

I was noticeably closer to the deck than I had ever been in an A-4. It usually takes a ten-foot ladder to approach the cockpit, but now the firemen were milling about looking down into the cockpit. One was tapping on the canopy.

"Hey doc! Open the goddamn canopy." There was no fire—no injury. What was all the excitement about?

Most naval aviators think they are indestructible. They think that a fatal accident is something that happens to someone else—someone who has just made an unforgivable error. Why else would they continue to play this crazy game?

I, too, am a naval aviator, and perhaps they are right! Perhaps I, too, am INDESTRUCTIBLE!

| 2 |

Flight Surgeon/Naval Aviator

From: BUPERS
To: COMCARAIRGRU FOUR
Info: U.S.S. *LEXINGTON* CVS 16
UNCLAS. LCDR GLENN F. KELLY, MC 538880/2100 DIRDET IN FEB
DIFOT AS NAVAL AVIATOR PROPORICH U.S.S. *LEXINGTON* CVS 16
ARREPCOVES DIFOT AS NAVAL AVIATOR REL . . .

There was no need to read further; the full impact of these dispatch orders hit me with the intensity of a lightning strike. All of my carefully laid plans were being destroyed in one quick stroke. I had already composed my letter of resignation from the Navy and had accepted a civil service position as a flight surgeon for the National Aeronautics and Space Administration in Houston. I was now being ordered to duty as senior medical officer aboard the U.S.S. *Lexington,* and the Navy would not accept my resignation until I had been at my new duty station for at least a year. As the impact of these orders began to descend like a dark cloud, I could feel the tide of anger rising.

The bastards! My quick Irish temper was beginning to show when a familiar Latin phrase silently entered my consciousness: *Illegitimus non carborundum.* This sage advice had been given to the Louisiana State University School of Medi-

cine, class of 1951, by Professor Red Akinhead. The acceptable translation of the Latin phrase was something like "Don't
let the bastards grind you down." The Navy translation was
even more descriptive, but the idea was the same. The grinder
could be your medical school professor, your senior officer,
or in this case, the Bureau of Medicine and Surgery (BUMED).
The dispatch orders were from the Bureau of Naval Personnel, as were all change-of-duty orders, but they were not given
without a nomination from the detail officer in BUMED. There
was no doubt in my mind who had initiated these orders.

Doctor Akinhead had left the class of '51 with a wealth of
practical advice and corny humor. As professor of internal
medicine, he was charged with making doctors out of a never-
ending group of kids fresh out of college. He liked to compare
teaching with throwing mud against a board fence: "The more
you throw, the more mud sticks to the fence." Enough had
stuck to most of the class of '51 to get us through four years
of medical school.

The anger seemed to dissolve as I thought of another saying that Professor Akinhead left with the class of '51: "It's a
long fight with a short stick, ain't it son?"

I didn't know that my fight had just begun when I graduated from medical school, and that I was going to need Red
Akinhead's advice every time I turned a corner. Now the
BUMED detail office was the illegitimate who was trying to
grind me down. This wasn't an impersonal decision of some
inanimate computer program; the Navy was not yet that
sophisticated. All flight surgeons were detailed by one Medical Corps' captain. This was the same captain who, after my
formal request to be considered for duty with NASA as a medical astronaut was disapproved, had refused to assign me to
NASA as a flight surgeon.

No, this wasn't a random impersonal assignment. BUMED
officials knew that I had already decided to resign my commission and accept the position with NASA. They also knew
that I couldn't resign for a full year after receiving a permanent change-of-duty orders—a full year! Project Mercury would
be over and planning for the Gemini Program would be well
underway; I would miss all of it. The delay might even de-
stroy my chances of being chosen when NASA finally decided
to select medical astronauts.

With these new thoughts, I realized that all of the anger
had not dissolved, and I was tempted to use the Navy translation of Dr. Akinhead's Latin. I also realized that any amount
of profanity wouldn't change things and would only make me
feel better temporarily. I had been taught that these words were

simply positive evidence of a severely limited vocabulary. Although my vocabulary contained an ample supply of colorful expletives, I rarely used them.

I had to be particularly careful when I taught the men's Bible class on Sunday mornings. The first Sunday after the carrier accident, I had presented a rather moving lesson of faith and divine purpose. I felt very strongly that I had a purpose in life to fulfill, and I thought I knew just what that purpose was, but what was the divine purpose of spending a year on a g- - - - - - - carrier?

In plain English this dispatch meant that, in less than a month, I had to sell my house, move the family to Pensacola, and report for duty as senior medical officer of the U.S.S. *Lexington*. There was some sadistic irony here that I could not bring myself to appreciate. Perhaps they wanted me to scrub the tire marks off the round down and otherwise repair the damage I had done to the flight deck. It was certain that no other senior medical officer had made a more dramatic entry onto his new duty station.

I rechecked the dates and realized that I actually had less than two weeks to report to the *Lexington*. There was no time to sell the house or move the family; that would have to come later.

I had known that the present senior medical officer of the *Lexington* had been acting strangely for a while. On a previous trip when I had accompanied the air group to the *Lexington* for carrier qualifications, the other physician had expressed concern. I was not surprised when it became necessary to admit the senior doctor for psychiatric evaluation. BUMED needed a senior medical officer for the U.S.S. *Lexington* quickly.

Commander of Carrier Air Group Four Captain "Bull" Werner was not unhappy with their selection. He had to answer too many of COMNAVAIRLANT's pointed questions about why a doctor was destroying his aircraft by flying them into carriers. Bull Werner had never been too fond of his young flight surgeon/naval aviator. A real naval aviator had to smoke cigars, drink beer, chase women, and cuss like a sailor; I did not fit into Bull Werner's mold. The senior medical officer at NAS Cecil Field—Captain Dick Nauman—did, and I suspected that he also was not too unhappy with the recent turn of events that would remove me from both of their commands.

As a lieutenant, junior grade, I had relieved Commander Nauman as flight surgeon of VR-8 in Hawaii eight years ago.

Now, Captain Nauman was my senior medical officer. Soon after arriving at Cecil Field, there had been an unpleasant confrontation. Captain Nauman wanted me to function as his assistant, to supervise the other medical officers, and to run the medical clinic. Unfortunately, I had different ideas on how I should spend my time at this stage of my career.

Although the discussion started amicably enough with a logical explanation of the requirements of the clinic and the need to further develop the young doctor's skill as a flight surgeon/naval aviator, the discussion increased in intensity and no satisfactory common ground could be found.

Captain Nauman's request was relatively straightforward. It was customary for the flight surgeon to divide his time between medical and squadron. He reported to the squadron or group commander for all administrative and command matters; however, for medical matters he reported to the senior medical officer and was assigned clinical duties as required.

The division of operational and clinical duties had to be worked out on a local level between the line commanders and the senior medical officers. This division of responsibility was always a problem for the flight surgeon, but it was an even more acute problem for the flight surgeon/naval aviator—his own personal safety was involved. He had to keep a high degree of proficiency in the aircraft in order to be safe; to do this, he had to participate in frequent, regular flights in high-performance aircraft.

At my previous duty station—the Naval Missile Center at Point Mugu, California—I had been one of three doctors serving over 4,000 active-duty personnel and their dependents. In addition, we provided the industrial medical support to over 4,000 civil service and other personnel employed in the various government contracts. There were operational problems in various missile systems that required aeromedical study, as well as many problems in the medical support of the Naval Missile Center and the Pacific Missile Range.

During this time, I had been able to assist in the establishment of the Life Sciences Department of the Naval Missile Center and head the Biomedical Division. While these activities were professionally rewarding, they left very little time to develop my new skills as a naval aviator.

It wasn't that I wanted to turn my back on medicine. Aerospace medicine is a medical specialty, just as thoracic surgery and opthalmology are. I considered the flight surgeon/naval aviator to be on the cutting edge of that specialty, and just as in other highly technical specialties, he had to go where the problems were. He had to participate actively in air operations;

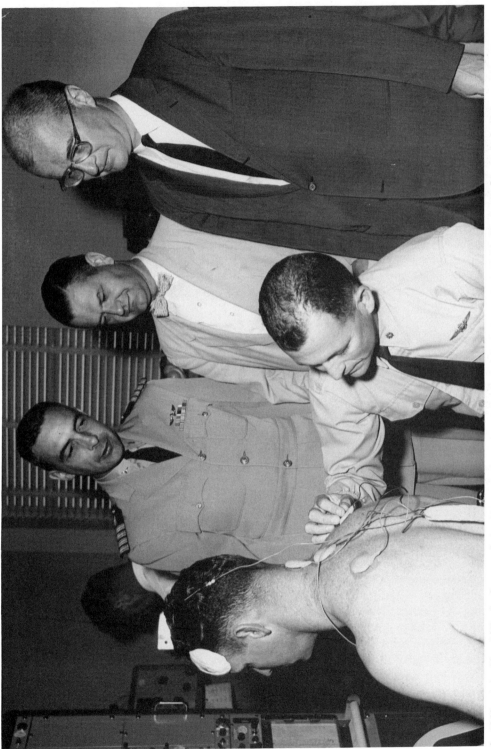

In 1959, at the Naval Missile Center, Point Mugu, California, Lieutenant Commander Fred Kelly, Medical Corps, U.S. Navy, prepares to record heart signals and brain waves from Lieutenant Bill Elliott during a test flight in the F4H Phantom II. Lieutenant Elliott wore the Navy Mark IV full pressure suit during these test flights. Observing, from left to right, are: Captain Carl Pruett, Medical Corps, U.S. Navy, Pacific Missile Range medical officer; Dr. Orr Reynolds, Department of Defense, director of Science, Research and Engineering; and Dr. Clark Randt, NASA Life Sciences director. Mr. Cliff Phipps, co-holder of the patent on the floating electrode with the author, is seen in the background. Similar bioinstrumentation was used during spaceflight. (Courtesy U.S. Navy)

he had to fly high-performance jet aircraft off carriers at night under instrument conditions and be familiar enough with the weapon system to use it if the need arose. Just as there were no shortcuts to a medical education, there was no room for compromise in training a high-performance jet pilot. In return, the flight surgeon/naval aviator would be in a position to give a level of insight into operational problems that could not be expected of a line naval aviator or a flight surgeon. I felt that, at this stage of my training, I could not do this and run Captain Nauman's dispensary. Now BUMED had assigned me to run the medical department on a carrier.

———

If I could force myself to look at it from BUMED's point of view, the choice was an obvious one, but dispatch orders? In Navy English, this meant: "Get your ass in gear."

———

I had heard these words before. In spite of my Southern Baptist background, I had developed a considerable vocabulary of such words. My two older brothers saw that I was indoctrinated early. They were three and five years older, and before I could give them much competition in a serious scrap, I could hold my own in a verbal exchange. My vocabulary expanded considerably when I lied about my age and worked as an arc welder in a shipyard. Even at the tender age of fifteen, I could swap stories with the most seasoned shipfitter, and could use language only a shipyard worker could appreciate and understand. I considered myself proficient in the language of the street—until my first flight with First Lieutenant John Leonard of the United States Marines. Then, I knew I had met the master of this dubious art form.

I had heard of Lieutenant Leonard's reputation through a cousin of my roommate at pre-flight. Jack Tolar had been my roommate and closest friend since we both reported to the Navy V-12 unit at Millsaps College and met in one of the interminable lines that are unavoidable for an apprentice seaman. Jack was the oldest of four boys and a girl, and his father was a diving coach in San Antonio, Texas. Jack, in his typically modest way, had explained that he was slower than the rest of his family—he didn't learn to do a two-and-a-half forward flip off the high board until he was five.

Dick (Bud) Currier was Jack's first cousin and nearly a year older. He lived nearby and served as the older brother Jack never had. They both had joined the Navy flight training program, and Bud was a class ahead of Jack in the Navy Pre-Flight School at Chapel Hill, North Carolina. Bud continued the big-brother role and decided to stay in the Navy when the first option was announced.

It was the end of 1945. The war was over and the Navy was left with more aviation cadets than the peacetime budget could afford. Officials announced that all aviation cadets could resign and be honorably discharged to continue their civilian life, or they could stay and flight training.

Jack wanted to return to college and prepare for the 1946 Olympics. Clarence Mabry and Bill Nobling, my other roommates, also decided to resign, as did most of my other close friends. For me, it wasn't a difficult decision at all. I had joined the Navy to fly. After a year in college and seven months in pre-flight, I was so close to realizing one of my first major goals that I couldn't quit. Bud Currier felt the same way—he stayed. It was good to have Bud as a ''big brother.''

Bud eagerly assumed this role and met me as soon as I arrived at the Glenview Naval Air Station, just north of Chicago, for primary flight training in the N2S Yellow Peril. ''I'll tell you, Fred, it's rough up here. They didn't get rid of enough cadets with the option, and now they are doing their best to wash them out. Whatever you do, don't get that Marine Lieutenant Leonard as your instructor. Half of his students don't even get to the solo stage.''

There was, of course, no way for a cadet to have any influence on instructor assignment, but both Bud and I were relieved when my instructor turned out to be a pleasant naval officer named Lieutenant Whiggens. We seemed to get along very well, and I thoroughly enjoyed my first three flights. On the debriefing after the third hop, Lieutenant Whiggens took me aside and told me that he was very pleased with my progress and considered me almost ready for solo.

The initial elation subsided as the instructor continued. ''Since I am leaving the Navy to go back to law school, a new instructor will have to be assigned. No, I don't know who the new instructor will be, but there will probably be several demo flights before he can clear you for solo.''

Dick and I were again relieved when Lieutenant Durant was assigned as my new instructor. This relief lasted until the debriefing from my first demo hop. Lieutenant Durant was being transferred to another duty station and another flight instructor would be assigned after this flight.

The next morning on the schedule board, there it was:

LEONARD/KELLY- - - - - -A5

There was no time for the impact of this development to sink in. "Kelly, I'm Leonard. Get your goddamn ass in gear." First Lieutenant Leonard was slightly taller than his new student, well built and erect, but with a slouchiness that was initially disarming. He was dressed in a well-worn flight uniform and a heavy flight jacket with a parachute slung over his shoulder. The most striking thing about him was his Clark Gable mustache, or maybe it was the look in his eyes. There was no doubt about it: the guy really thought he *was* Clark Gable! "I see you're from Louisiana. I took instructor training in New Orleans at Lakefront. You damned coonasses are a pain in the ass. I never saw one of you who could find your butt with both hands. Oh well, get your goddamn ass in gear and let's go."

With that exchange I lost my identity, and from that moment on, I was "that goddamn coonass." The gosport tube rattled with a string of obscenities that would make my shipyard friends blush. I didn't mind being called a coonass; I knew that this was Leonard's attempt at using the vulgar slang for the Louisiana Cajun. I'm not technically a Cajun, an ethnic group descended from the French Acadians, because I'm mostly Irish. I've had many friends who are Cajuns; only the uninformed would consider the term derogatory. If the Marine wanted to call me a coonass, I would take it as a compliment.

The tirade of obscenities was continuous throughout every flight. Although the N2S had no radio and few other instruments, the gosport tube served as an effective intercom. It was simply a rubber hose that had a speaking port at one end, while the other end was connected to the ear pads built into the student's soft leather headgear. The student could hear instructions over the wind noise and the roar of the engine if the instructor spoke loudly enough. This Marine flight instructor had no trouble making himself heard.

This communications system was entirely one way, and there was no way for the instructor to hear the student. In my case that was very fortunate indeed. Had Lieutenant Leonard been able to hear some of the choice shipyard phrases coming back at him, one more of the jarhead's cadets would not have made it to his first solo flight.

I made it to solo, completed primary flight training, and moved up to the SNJ advanced trainer at NAS Corpus Christi, Texas. Next was the PBY Catalina at NAS Banana River, Florida, and then the F8F Bearcat. After five flights in the advanced trainer, I was faced with another dilemma. The Navy still had to cut back, so I was given another option. I could resign now and return to civilian life, or I could continue flight training and sign up to serve another four years after graduation. I wanted to continue flying—I particularly wanted to progress to the PBY and the Bearcat—but I also wanted to return to college and perhaps even go to medical school.

Again, it was good to turn to my adopted big brother. After a long discussion, Bud had said: "Fred, I'm going to stay in because I want to spend my whole life being a naval aviator. I love to fly, and I don't want to do anything else with my life, but let's face it, if you stay in you will have committed four and a half or five more years to the Navy, and the chances of you quitting at that stage to go back to medical school are just about nonexistent. It's your decision. I hope you stay in for selfish reasons, but if you don't, I can understand."

Six years later, as Lieutenant, Junior Grade, Fred Kelly, Medical Corps, United States Navy, I had served my internship at the U.S. Naval Hospital in Pensacola, Florida, and had graduated from the Navy's School of Aviation Medicine as a flight surgeon. It was good to be back in naval aviation, particularly as a flight surgeon.

———

I remembered my first encounter with a navy flight surgeon. "Just sit there. The flight surgeon wants to see you again." The slightly irritated voice of the medical attendant confirmed that there might be a problem.

"Is there a problem?"

Again the attendant avoided my question and repeated, "Just sit there. The doctor will see you in a minute."

The tone of his voice did little to lessen my anxiety. There can't be a problem! Not now! I've passed all the other tests. Only five out of a whole roomful of students passed the battery of aptitude tests when they gave it at LSU. None of my close friends made it. The examiner couldn't tell me my score, but he did say I had scored very high. His smile confirmed that the Navy wings of gold were within my reach. I only had to pass a simple physical exam, and I would be on my way to flight training.

The flight physical examination was given in Dallas, Texas; so the five from The Ole War School had been joined by groups from other Louisiana colleges and transported to big Dallas.

There couldn't be a problem! I'm so close. I know I don't have any medical problem. Who is this—what did he call him—flight surgeon? What's a flight surgeon? Probably some 4F who couldn't even get in the Navy. Probably not even a real doctor.

"Kelly, the flight surgeon can see you now—*Kelly*, the doctor's waiting."

"Yes, sir! Sorry sir!" One look at the medical attendant told me that he wasn't impressed by my military bearing; he just wanted me to move it.

As I entered the small military office crowded with a desk, an examining table, a bookcase, and very little else, I could see a concerned expression on the doctor's face. He was looking over his glasses at the physical examination form. I knew he was 4F. He did have a military uniform on under his white coat and some insignia on his shirt collar. The doctor spoke without looking up. "Why do you want to be a naval aviator?"

"Sir! Because they are the best, sir!" I wondered if I wasn't over doing it a bit, but at this point I had nothing to lose. It must have worked, because the doctor put down the paper and actually looked at me. He seemed to be studying me as if he were deciding my whole future. He was!

The doctor spoke again, "Why do you say that?"

"Sir, I've studied every plane the Navy has. I've made models of most of them. To fly planes like that, you have to be the best." I forgot to say sir again, but the doctor didn't seem to mind.

"Do you think you have what it takes to be a naval aviator?"

I didn't expect this question. Certainly, I did. I wouldn't be here if I didn't. (Careful. Don't sound too cocky.) "Yes, sir."

"Well, sit down here son, and let's talk about this a while." I must have given the right answer. He actually seemed to be trying to help me. Maybe he's not 4F after all—and he acts like a real doctor. "You know you have a problem with your eye exam." He read the puzzled expression on my face and continued: "Oh, your vision is OK, but your accommodation is a little out of limits."

"Sir, what is accommodation? I don't understand." The doctor explained that accommodation was the ability to bring close objects into sharp focus. I had been working on model airplanes for years and had never had any trouble seeing near objects. After some discussion, the doctor explained the test to me again and let me retake it.

The doctor seemed to be nearly as happy as I was when I passed the repeat test with no trouble. "Son, you know I called you back in here to tell you that you had failed the test and would not be accepted for flight training."

"Yes, sir, I know that, and I hope you know how much this means to me." I stood there for a moment trying to find a way to thank this man who they called a flight surgeon. No words came.

The doctor signed the papers and waved me out. "I know, son, I know." And I think he did.

There was never anything but naval aviation. My older brother had joined the Army Air Corps and was dropping bombs on Germany. The B-17 was slow and had no maneuverability; it was a sitting duck for the fast German fighters. In his infrequent letters, he noticeably failed to offer any encouragement that might entice his younger brother into the Air Corps. We both knew that his was a valuable part of the war effort, but it wasn't for me.

Naval aviation was different. If you had to fight—and in 1943 there was no option—naval aviation was the way to go. Even before the war clouds began to gather, the high ceilings of the old farmhouse were spotted with flying models of the latest Grumman aircraft. As many as thirty models at any one time had been made of balsa wood and covered with tissue paper, and were hanging from a thread tacked to the beaded wooden ceiling. As the war progressed and newer models came out, there would be an occasional Army fighter like the Mustang or the Lightning and even an occasional B-25, but the scene was always dominated by the Hellcat, the TBM, or the SB2C dive bomber. Then there was the magnificent model of the F4U Corsair with its inverted gull wings; the great radial, air-cooled engine; and the monstrous propeller.

The Air Corps had insisted on using the liquid-cooled engine on most of its fighters, while the Navy saw an advantage in the reliability of the simpler, air-cooled engine. The Navy also built more substantial aircraft, which, in addition to taking the abuse of repeated carrier landings, could absorb considerable enemy fire and still fly, fight, and make it back to the carrier.

The aircraft carrier had been proved to be an effective instrument of war by the Japanese on December 7, 1941. To the Allies, Pearl Harbor was an unspeakable act of barbarism, but to the Japanese it was a brilliant tactical operation that very nearly won the war before it was declared. To the entire world, it demonstrated that the aircraft carrier had become an awesome weapon. The war would be fought and won in the air. In the wide expanse of the Pacific, it was the carrier task force that would be a deciding factor.

It was good to be back in naval aviation!

This feeling was tempered by a letter from Jack Tolar that was written just after the Olympic diving trials in 1946. During the trials, Jack had received word that Bud had added power to the F8F during a carrier wave off and had not been able to hold enough rudder to counteract the powerful torque of the engine; in an instant he had rolled and was in the water. There was no chance for survival. Jack had tried to continue his dives because he knew Bud would have wanted him to, but the timing was not there—neither was the heart.

A more recent letter brought better news. Jack had completed his master's degree in physical education and had decided to change the course of his life once more. He had been accepted as a freshman student in the University of Texas School of Medicine at Galveston. He had also changed his religious denomination and felt a strong calling to be Southern Baptist medical missionary.

I had often reflected on this turn of events. Later, when Jack had completed his boards in thoracic surgery and was accepted as a missionary to Nairobi, we met and had a long talk about this twist of fate. Jack has said it first. ''No one in our group at Millsaps or at pre-flight would have been surprised if the quite, introspective kid from Louisiana had ended up with the foreign mission board.'' But Tolar! He had much more flash. Certainly, he was the center of attention whenever a diving board was handy. He loved it! How could he possibly bury his talents in some African jungle?

Jack was on his way to Nairobi, and he seemed to get vicarious pleasure over my new orders. My application to return to flight training had been approved; I was on my way back to Pensacola. I was getting a second chance to win my wings of gold.

The next eighteen months were the most demanding period in my entire career. It was particularly demanding, physically and psychologically. I was attempting to do something at age thirty, with a wife and three small children, which possibly should have been reserved for a kid of eighteen.

Finally, on a cold February morning in 1958, my daughter pinned the coveted wings of gold on my uniform. I could feel a deep sense of pride, mixed with relief, that the goal set so many years ago had finally been realized.

I was now a naval flight surgeon and a designated naval aviator, qualified in high-performance jet aircraft, with orders to a research position at the Naval Missile Center. There was hushed talk about a manned space program that would try to launch men into space from a place in Florida near the old Banana River Navel Air Station. A new goal began to compete for my attention. Who could understand the physiological problems of space flight better than a doctor who was also an experienced jet pilot?

———————

I glanced down at the dispatch orders in my hand and was brought back to the present with a jolt.

Illegitimus non carborundum!

The anger returned, but so did the determination. This would only be a slight detour of my journey to space flight. A year at the very heart of naval aviation—the aircraft carrier—might not be so bad. It might even be exciting.

| 3 |

The Astronaut's Flight Surgeon

One year later, the senior medical officer of the U.S.S. *Lexington* was transferred to the Naval Reserve and was ready to begin a new career as a NASA flight surgeon. For me, it had been a busy year—I had worked hard. There had been more emergency calls of "Crash on the flight deck" than I thought were necessary, but it had been an exciting and professionally rewarding year. I had developed a close rapport with the pilots and with the ship's company, and I had won the confidence and support of the command. I was ready for a new challenge—in Houston.

The Kellys arrived in Houston during March of 1964, shortly after the newly established Manned Spaceflight Center had moved into the new complex of buildings at Clear Lake. This was an area about 30 miles south of Houston on the way to Galveston, and other than a few scattered communities like Webster, Seabrook, and Laporte, there was nothing. Del Webb was building Clear Lake City in typical Del Webb style with elaborate plans for shopping centers, schools, and recreation centers with gymnasiums, swimming pools, and a golf course; but so far, there were only a few apartments and a sea of red mud. There was one new motel on the main road (renamed NASA Road One); so after the family was settled at the motel, I went to check in at NASA's Manned Spaceflight Center.

"So you're going to work for Dr. Berry. Go right on up to the eighth floor. You can't miss his office." The pretty receptionist had no way of knowing she had said anything wrong, but she couldn't help but notice an unusual expression on the face of NASA's newest employee as I turned toward the elevators. I wished she had said "working *with* Dr. Berry." Chuck had been a friend for years before we were both selected in May of 1960 to be medical monitors on the Mercury Project. Along with twenty-eight other aeromedical specialists, we had been asked to help the three flight surgeons attached to the Space Task Group at the Langley Research Center monitor the physiological responses of the Mercury astronauts.

Stan White had headed the flight surgeons at Langley since November of 1958, and Bill Douglas served as the Mercury astronauts' flight surgeon. Both Stan and Bill were detailed from the U.S. Air Force. At the insistence of Stan, Chuck resigned his Air Force Commission and joined the group as a civilian. The Army sent a bright young flight surgeon named Bill Augerson to the team. The Navy had been asked to supply a flight surgeon, but BUMED officials, in their infinite wisdom, had determined that they could not spare a flight surgeon and sent a psychologist instead.

When the move to Houston came in July of 1962, Stan concentrated on flight hardware, such as space suit improvement and instrumentation system development in a division he called Life Systems, while Chuck became chief of the Aerospace Medical Operations Office.

The receptionist was right. I was going to work *for* Chuck Berry. Chuck had firmly established himself as the head of Medical Operations and enjoyed his growing reputation as "The Astronaut's Flight Surgeon." He was also gaining a reputation with some of the other aerospace medicine specialists for using his position to broaden his own professional prestige. His name appeared on a number of scientific papers that were written by his staff. This situation caused some discontentment, but I had no trouble dismissing it as common practice in most professional organizations. Chuck was the head of the department. He had proved himself a good politician— he gave convincing talks and made a profound impression on his audience whether they were the general public, visiting dignitaries, or other divisional chiefs within NASA. No other part of NASA needed to improve its image more than Medical Operations, and Chuck was the man to do it.

Our collective reputation had been more than tarnished

In May of 1960, a group of medical doctors was selected for training as aeromedical flight controllers. They were assigned to assist the Space Task Group physicians to monitor physiological responses of Mercury astronauts during spaceflight—the first space surgeons. The training was given at Cape Canaveral, Florida, and at NASA's Langley Research Center, Virginia. Seated, from left to right, are: Jacques Sherman, Ed Overholt, Vance Marchbanks, Hal Ellingson, Walt Jones, Astronaut John Glenn, Tom Davis, Bill Turner, Carl Pruett, and Clyde Kratochvil. Standing, left to right, are: Walt Brewer, Bill Hall, John Lane, Bob Moser, Chuck Berry, Lou Herrman, Frank Austin, Duane Graveline, Art Grote, Fritz Holmstrom, Dick Day, Larry Lamb, Bob Burwell, Royce Hawkins, John Lawson, Roy Kelly, Julian Ward, Harry Brett, John Gordon, Warren Bishop, Bill Shea, Jack Robbins, Smokey Dunn, Dick Hansen, George Smith, Bob Unger, Ed Beckman, and Fred Kelly. One of these doctors, Duane Graveline, would be chosen as a medical astronaut. (Courtesy NASA)

Flight Director Christopher Columbus Craft (seated) explains the operation of one of the monitoring consoles in Mercury Control Center at Cape Canaveral, Florida, to the Mercury astronauts. Standing, from left to right, are: Astronauts Donald Slayton, Wally Schirra, Gus Grissom, Alan Shepard, John Glenn, Scott Carpenter, and Gordon Cooper. (Courtesy NASA)

The seven Mercury astronauts—three Naval aviators, three Air Force pilots, and one Marine aviator. All were experienced military aviators with test pilot training; all indestructible. First row, from left to right, are: Walter H. Schirra, Jr., Donald K. Slayton, John H. Glenn, Jr., and M. Scott Carpenter. Second row: Alan B. Shepard, Jr., Virgil I. Grissom, and L. Gordon Cooper. (Courtesy NASA)

Astronaut Gus Grissom, in the Mercury space suit, prepares to enter the Navy centrifuge at Johnsville, Pennsylvania, to experience the gravitational forces expected during his flight in the Mercury capsule. Every Mercury astronaut was given extensive training at this facility before spaceflight. (Courtesy NASA)

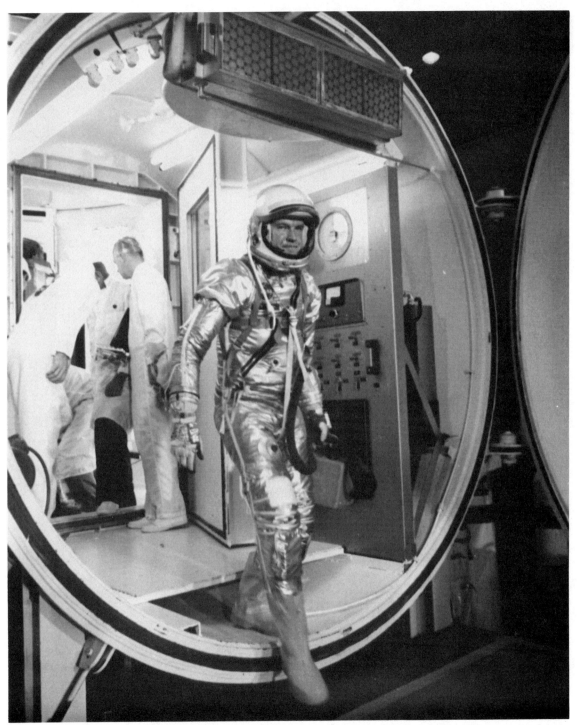

Astronaut Gordon Cooper leaves the altitude chamber at Cape Canaveral after a test of the Mercury space suit. This suit was an adaptation of the Navy Mark IV full pressure suit. (Courtesy NASA)

Astronaut Gordon Cooper tests his mobility in the Mercury space suit while pressurized to 5 PSI. The suit was designed to automatically pressurize if the Mercury capsule failed to maintain pressure. Mobility and comfort in the space suits were steadily improved during the Gemini and Apollo programs. (Courtesy NASA)

Operation and training flights in high-performance military jets were an important part of astronaut training. From left to right, are: Mercury astronauts Scott Carpenter, Gordon Cooper, John Glenn, Gus Grissom, Wally Schirra, Alan Shepard, and Deke Slayton. Four astronauts would lose their lives in aircraft accidents: Ted Freeman, Charlie Bassett, Elliott See, and Gene Williams. (Courtesy NASA)

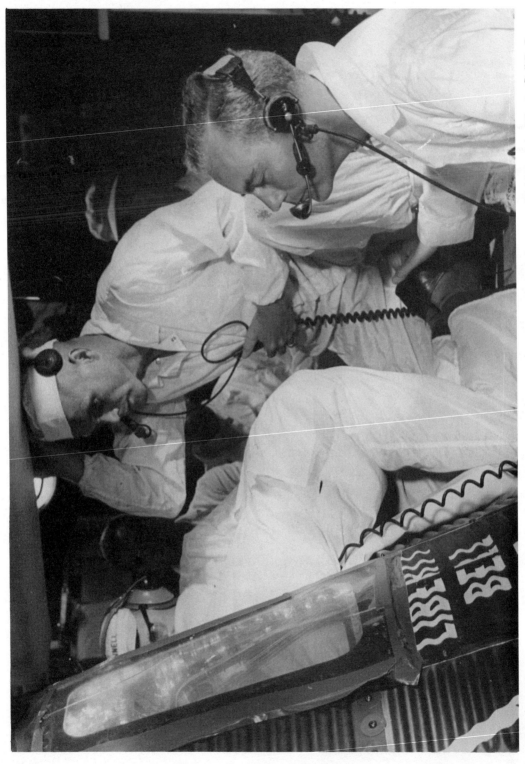

Astronaut John Glenn and Dr. Bill Douglas observe as Astronaut Grissom is being prepared for a pre-flight test in Liberty Bell 7. Dr. Douglas was one of the three physicians assigned to the Space Task Group and served as one of the Mercury astronauts' flight surgeons. In keeping with the low-profile characteristic of medical researchers, NASA archives contain no photographic documentation of their many contributions. (Courtesy NASA)

by a little-known incident that happened early in the Mercury Project involving a chimpanzee named Enos. It was the final checkout of the Mercury capsule and tracking network before John Glenn was to make his orbital flight. Christopher C. Kraft was the flight director (the C. stands for Columbus), and we were exercising the entire network of remote monitoring sites. It was a dress rehearsal for the first manned orbital space flight. The world's attention was riveted on this historic event.

This flight was responsible for Chuck Yeager's now famous statement to a reporter who asked if he would like to fly in the Mercury spacecraft. Yeager reportedly drawled something to the effect that he "didn't want to fly anything that you had to dust the monkey chips off the seat before you could sit down." This spacecraft was outfitted with a special couch designed for Enos, and it even had a set of controls. The controls were not for controlling the spacecraft, as Yeager had insinuated, but for sending back a series of coded messages that we could use to learn much more about the chimp's performance than we could about any astronaut's performance on the later, manned flights.

The group of "chimp astronauts" had undergone a period of intensive training in the centrifuge, in flight simulators, and in a variety of other gadgets that only a dedicated group of medical researchers could devise. Enos emerged as the clear leader of the chimps; his selection was as obvious as the selection of John Glenn to make the orbital flight.

The medical monitors, who later would be called aeromedical flight controllers, had never before seen a chimp's electrocardiogram, but they were assured that it was similar to a human's. During all of the pre-flight testing, the researchers had never seen so much as a premature ventricular contraction (PVC) on Enos. There was no reason to expect that any abnormalities would develop on this flight.

I was assigned to the U.S. Naval Ship *Rose Knot Victor* (RKV), which was an aging cargo ship modified to house the latest instrumentation gear. It was, in fact, a complete tracking site that could be moved from one position to another to meet the demands of a particular mission. For this flight it was stationed in the middle of the Atlantic Ocean. As the RKV Surgeon, I could expect to see six minutes of data on each of three orbits and was to relay my findings by teletype messages to the Mission Control Center, which had been set up at Cape Canaveral, Florida. Data would also be relayed to each of the other monitoring sites selectively spread at strategic locations around the orbital path.

After meeting the ship in Antigua and steaming east for

Enos, a 5-year-old chimpanzee, is fitted into his pressure couch prior to his spaceflight in the Mercury capsule. He was selected from a group of five chimps that had been trained for the flight. Some of the medical instrumentation that was used compromised the flight, and the incident gave the astronauts reason to distrust medical researchers. (Courtesy NASA)

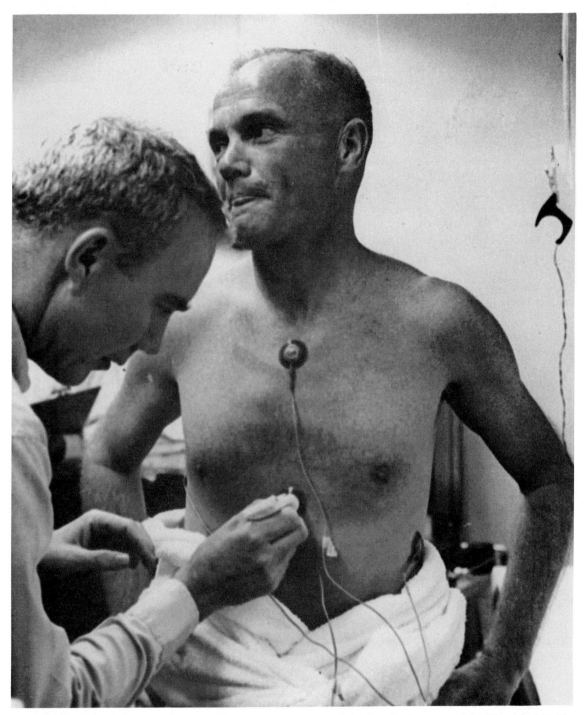

As he prepares to follow Enos into orbit in the Mercury capsule, it is time for Astronaut John Glenn to bite his lip. Prior to his historic flight in Friendship 7, John is instrumented for electrocardiographic tracings by the Mercury astronauts' flight surgeon, Dr. Bill Douglas. (Courtesy NASA)

seven days, we arrived at our assigned position well before launch. There were simulations, systems checkouts, network checkouts, and more simulations. The *Rose Knot Victor* and its team of flight controllers were ready—the spacecraft was not. A two-week delay was announced and all the flight controllers in the states and Bermuda could go home; those in Hawaii and Australia could go to the beach or have a party; those on the *Rose Knot Victor* could not even make it to the nearest land and get back for the new launch date. There we sat.

Monotony was broken by table tennis in the number three hold with ambient temperatures ranging on the far side of 110 degrees Fahrenheit and the deck rolling 20 to 30 degrees from the horizontal. It was also broken by one of the merchant marine seaman who went into the acute episode of paranoid schizophrenia and attacked himself and other crewmen with a meat cleaver. After sedation and a tendon repair, he was kept under twenty-four-hour guard, and the ship was able to stay on position without further incident.

The team of NASA flight controllers had been aboard the *Rose Knot Victor* for twenty-five long days when the time finally came for the flight. Countdown and launch were uneventful, and during his first pass over the ship, Enos *looked* good. His electrocardiogram was normal by human standards; his respiration was regular; and his psychomotor performance data indicated that he was performing satisfactorily.

Just before loss of signal (LOS), he was evidently distracted from one of his tasks, and when he fell behind, he received a healthy shock from the electrodes attached to his feet. Another indication that problems were developing occurred about ten minutes later when the surgeon from the station in Zanzibar, Africa, reported that he had seen several premature ventricular contractions on the electrocardiogram. These abnormal beats continued to be reported from each tracking site, and during the second pass over the RKV, there were many single PVCs and several runs of four abnormal beats in a row. There was also an indication that the abnormal beats were being initiated from at least two different areas in his heart. In a human, this indication would confirm a diagnosis of ventricular tachycardia and would require immediate treatment; if untreated, it could be expected to progress into ventricular fibrillation and death.

––––––

Had this been a training simulation, it would have been a better one than I was able to devise at Langley. Before Alan

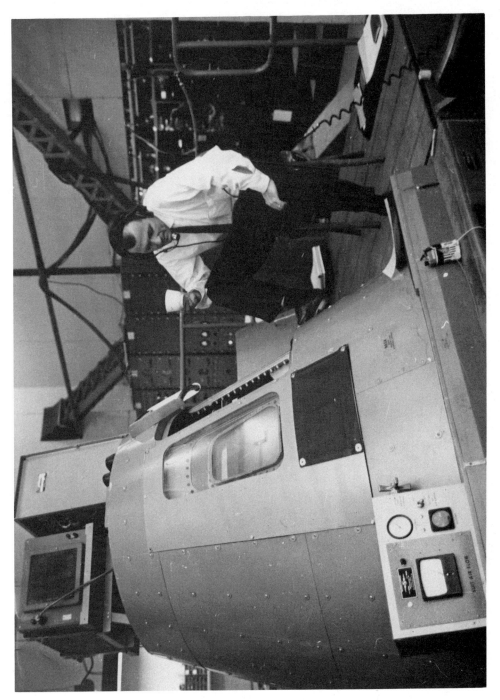

Simulated medical emergencies are used to train aeromedical flight controllers for problems expected during spaceflight. Here, the author coaches astronauts in the Mercury capsule simulator to make the simulations more realistic and "fool the flight surgeons." (Courtesy NASA)

Shepard's flight, I had been assigned temporarily at Langley to develop a training program for the medical monitors. By using some of the astronaut's biomedical tapes collected in pressure chambers and centrifuges, taking them out of context and adding some dialogue, I was able to make convincing simulations. Of course, I had no grossly abnormal electrocardiographic tracings such as the one I was now facing, but with the help of the astronauts, the scripts became believable.

Some of the astronauts seemed to enjoy reading the script and ad-libbing answers to the surgeon's questions. John Glenn particularly enjoyed having a simulated heart attack. The slow heart rate and escape beats were perfectly normal while resting for long periods in an altitude chamber, but when John complained of acute pain in his left chest radiating down his arm, accompanied by periods of unresponsiveness, it was a different matter. Even though each of the physicians was a specialist and had extensive training in cardiology, none expected to see an abnormal-appearing electrocardiogram on John Glenn during a simulation.

———

But this was no simulation, and even though the patient was a chimpanzee, he was a very important chimp. I turned to the other flight surgeon aboard the RKV. "So they've never seen a PVC on Enos during his training simulations! He must have been saving it for the real thing. Royce, check me on this tracing. These are multifocal premature ventricular contractions, aren't they? And this is ventricular tachycardia. You agree? I think the chimp is in real trouble." Major Hawkings nodded agreement, and Mission Control was notified of our findings and of our recommendation that the flight be terminated early.

The flight was terminated after the second orbit because of an attitude control problem (the failure of a roll reaction jet) and an indication that an inverter was overheating. The attitude was right for retrofire at the end of the second orbit, but the flight director could not be sure that the attitude would again be correct at the end of the third orbit for a nominal end-of-mission retrofire.

It was not until the mission debriefing at Langley that Bill Augerson told the flight controllers Enos had been instrumented for central venous pressure. This act was done by a medical researcher who has managed to remain nameless. The catheter was placed into a large vein in the chimp's leg

Astronaut John Glenn and Dr. Bill Douglas check Glenn's pressure suit in the astronauts' quarters before the first manned orbital flight in the Mercury capsule. (Courtesy NASA)

by the overdiligent researcher who wanted to make sure it had no chance of coming out; it was passed up the leg into the vena cava, through the right atrium of his heart, into the right ventricle, and out into the lungs through the pulmonary artery. With every beat of his heart, this tube was moving back and forth, causing the premature contractions, and at the very least, distracting him from his performance task—then there were those damned electrical shocks!

Christopher Kraft was livid, and so was everyone else associated with Project Mercury. Had we lost Enos on this flight, there would have been no way to get a "go" to launch John Glenn; the whole Mercury Project would have been set back months, and maybe years. Medical researchers were not to be trusted. Dr. Charles Berry had a difficult job ahead of him if NASA was ever to get a meaningful aerospace medical research program going. As the newest member of Chuck's medical operations team, I was going to give him all the support I could.

With my new titles as NASA Flight Surgeon and Supervisory Aerospace Medical Officer, I was finally settled in my new office. It was not on the eighth floor with Chuck, but across the campuslike quadrangle in a two-story building that housed flight medicine, occupational medicine, and the photo lab. I could look out my large picture window and see the headquarters building; there, on the eighth floor at the far end, was Chuck's office. This was the first time I had had a chance to sit down and reflect on my recent move.

I was suddenly distracted by what appeared to be a bullet hole in my plate glass window. On closer examination it was not a hole, but a cleverly applied applique which closely resembled an incoming bullet hole. When I boresighted the hole from the center of my chair, the phantom shot appeared to have been fired from the end office on the eighth floor of the headquarters building—the office of Dr. Charles A. Berry. Someone had a wild sense of humor. I was going to like it here.

| 4 |

Flight Medicine

In March of 1964 when the Kellys arrived in Houston, the third group of astronauts had been selected and were beginning their new career. The new astronauts faced most of the same problems that Jimi and I faced, with at least one notable exception. Del Webb had offered each of them the use of one of the tract houses on a promotional deal. A few of them accepted the offer and moved into Clear Lake City while they were building their own homes in one of the more elite subdivisions of El Lago or the newly opened Nassau Bay. Mr. Webb did not offer the same deal to the Kellys; so we settled for a rental apartment on Buccaneer Drive.

It was true that the year aboard the *Lexington* had caused me to miss the last flight of Project Mercury, but if I was worried about my involvement in the planning stage of the Gemini Program, I need not have concerned myself. From my first day on the job I was, as my Cajun friends would have said, up to my eyeballs in alligators. Flight medicine was a good place to start because we took care of the astronauts and their families. It was an excellent chance to get to know each of them personally and professionally. I knew the Mercury astronauts and some of the second group. Jim Lovell had been the safety officer for VF101 before his selection. VF101 was a fighter training squadron attached to Bull Werner's Carrier Air Group, and

as the Group's flight surgeon, I had worked with Jim on flight safety problems.

Jimi and I felt closer to the third group because they, too, were just getting settled: finding a house, finding a school for the kids, and adapting to the NASA way of doing things. In many ways it was much like reporting to a new military duty station. Most of the astronauts were from the Air Force or the Navy, and it was perfectly natural for them to include the new flight surgeon in their round of parties; they hadn't learned yet that doctors were not to be trusted.

Astronaut Dave Scott, however, had second thoughts when the new flight surgeon showed up at his party with a blond wife instead of the brunette he remembered. After Jimi convinced him that she was wearing a blond wig, he smiled apologetically and invited us in. This incident gave me an insight into David Scott's character which was not included in his medical record: Scandal was to be avoided at all cost. The public, and possibly the astronauts themselves, had not yet realized that they were not some breed of infallible creature who somehow was immune to the social problems that infect other parts of suburban America. This part of their education would come later.

The flight medicine clinic was headed by Dr. Howie Minners, and as the newest NASA flight surgeon, I was assigned to work with him. There were a number of other flight surgeons who worked in one capacity or another. The number and names kept varying from time to time; so an actual count was difficult. It soon became evident that none of us could stay very close to a particular job description because of the diversity of our commitments and the tasks which should have been taken care of weeks or months before. The care of the astronauts and their families took priority right after emergencies, but there were always urgent meetings that should have medical representation, tests that needed medical coverage, and position papers that had a deadline. The Gemini Program was moving; if there were no medical inputs, the program would go forward without them.

It also became obvious that there was no such thing as The NASA Flight Surgeon, or The Gemini Flight Surgeon; certainly, none could claim the title of The Astronaut's Flight Surgeon. It also became evident that the rapid turnover of physicians must be based on something more than the normal rotation of medical officers on loan from the services. I soon lost my title as NASA's newest flight surgeon. The Manned Spaceflight Center should have been an ideal place for someone interested in space medicine to spend his career; nevertheless, excellent flight surgeons seemed to come and go at an alarming rate for a variety of stated reasons. Those of us who remained were much too busy to spend time on this problem, but it did make us wonder.

I knew why I had come to Houston. Space flight would be increasing in duration and in complexity, which would bring more medically related problems that the young specialty of aerospace medicine must be ready to solve. What could be more logical than to select a doctor as a crew member? Why not select one who is an active NASA flight surgeon; who has been involved in the space program from the beginning; and who is a current jet pilot in the Navy Reserves and a carrier pilot? (Maybe I shouldn't mention the carrier.)

It might have been because of my personal bias, but I noticed that naval aviators seemed to have an edge on those who had been selected from the Air Force or the Marines when it came to party conversation. The talk was always about flying, and carrier operations were a facet that only the naval aviators could speak about with authority.

Another flight surgeon came to NASA from duty aboard a carrier and was therefore qualified to speak at astronaut parties—Dr. D. O. (Nig) Coons had been a medical officer aboard Canada's only carrier when he was persuaded, by Chuck Berry, to add his considerable talent to NASA's manned spaceflight efforts. To do so he had to resign his commission, leave a promising career in the Canadian Armed Forces Medical Service, and move to Houston. Nig and Betty Coons had arrived in Houston about the same time that the second group of astronauts were selected; so he became more closely associated with that group. They had settled in El Lago next to Ed White and Neil Armstrong. Jim Lovell and Tom Stafford lived nearby, as did Stan White and Chuck Berry.

I had to ask Nig to spell his nickname and explain how he came to adopt such an unusual name. In his crisp English Canadian accent, he explained. "The spelling is N-I-G. It's short for negro, you know. Some of my American friends started calling me that in postgraduate school, and it stuck. I think it has something to do with my last name." I understood very well. Nig wore his acquired name with the same sort of pride and determination that I had displayed when my primary flight instructor insisted on calling me "that goddamn coonass." I was secretly glad that my acquired name had not stuck.

It was easy to like this energetic Canadian. He approached each problem with a vigor and aggressiveness that was hard to match. Even if the task at hand was walking to the NASA cafeteria, I found it difficult to keep pace with this remarkable man. For the next four years, through many reorganizations and office name changes, I would work closely with, and for, Nig. We both worked *for* Chuck.

| 5 |

Nassau Bay

Jimi had, in her practiced, efficient way, managed to get the Kellys settled in the small apartment on Buccaneer Drive. Danny, Dewey, and Diane were enrolled in their respective schools. The new supermarket had opened in Clear Lake City; so it was no longer necessary to go to Houston for groceries. Jimmielene Black Kelly had practiced this routine sixteen times in twenty-nine years and had become quite proficient at moving and settling into a new environment.

If that wasn't enough to occupy her time, the search for a "permanant" home certainly was. We had decided to build a tract home on Del Webb's golf course. While I was getting settled into my new position, Jimi was trying to negotiate a few changes in the stock plans that would make the home more suitable to our needs. When she found it necessary to call Del Webb personally and complain about the inflexibility of his local representatives, I knew we would not be satisfied with a tract home. The next day we had our deposit returned and were sure that, wherever we settled, it would not be in Del Webb's Clear Lake City.

Nassau Bay was a new subdivision just across NASA Road One from the NASA center. They were beginning to sell lots, and a few houses were springing up. Several of the astronauts had purchased lots and were negotiating with builders. Most of the roads were in; most of the lots were surveyed and marked. The sales office was in a large house built for speculation and near the site of the new Nassau Bay Baptist church. Nassau Bay had the potential of being one of the nicest areas in greater Houston. The lots were large and wooded, on winding roads, and near a saltwater inlet connecting to the gulf. There was even a small freshwater lake on the site where an old farmhouse had been years before. The lots around the lake were particularly beautiful, with large oaks covered with Spanish moss. It reminded us of an old plantation site on the Mississippi River in Louisiana.

My salary as a GS-15 at NASA was slightly lower than my Navy pay had been and was simply not enough to afford this kind of living; so we, reluctantly, crossed Nassau Bay off our list and continued to look elsewhere. However, neither Jimi nor I could completely get Nassau Bay off our minds. It seemed that no matter where we looked, we always ended our search by driving through Nassau Bay and looking at the lots around the lake.

| 6 |

Medical Operations

"Hawaii Cap Com, this is Gemini Three, over."

"Gemini Three, this is Hawaii Cap Com, over."

"Hawaii Cap Com, this is Gemini Three Command Pilot, I need to talk to your surgeon."

Responding to a quick nod from the Capsule Communicator, Colonel Jack Ord, U.S. Air Force, Medical Corps, pressed the push-to-talk button. "Gemini Three, this is Hawaii Surgeon, over."

"Hey, doc! Ever since we lost contact with Canarvon, I've had a real bad headache, and now I feel sick at my stomach."

"Gemini Three, Hawaii Surgeon, where is the headache?"

"Doc, it's right in the middle of my head, and it's getting worse. What should I do?"

"Gemini Three, Hawaii Surgeon, can you tell me if the headache is steady or throbbing?" Doctor Ord knew he had less than six minutes to make a diagnosis before loss of signal; he wanted to make every question count. He turned to the systems engineer and asked him to check the environmental control system (ECS) readings.

"Doc, it's steady and I feel like I'm going to pass out."

"Gemini Three Pilot, this is Hawaii Surgeon, do you have any symptoms?"

"Hawaii Surgeon, this is Gemini Three Pilot, I have a dull

headache and a little dizziness, too."

"Hey doc! Gus has passed out and is shaking all over! What can I do? I don't feel too good either . . ."

"Gemini Three, this is Hawaii Surgeon, check your cabin pressure!"

"Gemini Three, this is Hawaii Surgeon, over."

"Gemini Three! This is Hawaii Surgeon, did you copy?"

"Gemini Three! Hawaii Surgeon! Over . . ."

There was no response. His instruments were reading zero. He had LOS and, for the first time, noticed the beads of sweat on his high forehead.

"OK Jack, you were right on track that time when you asked about the ECS. Systems would have normally helped but we aren't training systems today. You have cabin pressure on your console. What did it read?"

Jack looked at me with a sheepish grin. "Fred, you are really getting to be a hardnose."

"Well, I know you can't become an expert on all of the Gemini systems in a few days, but I think that the surgeons should know just about as much about the environmental control system as anyone. Now let's rewind the tape of this pass and have our debriefing."

Jack smiled and relaxed a little. He knew that during the actual mission he would probably never be required to talk on the air-to-ground loop. All communications would be taken care of by the capsule communicator (Cap Com) who, in most cases, would be one of the astronauts and would be the recognized leader of the remote-site flight controller team. On each remote site there would be a capsule communicator, a systems engineer, and two surgeons.

The Cap Com and systems engineer would be NASA employees or astronauts assigned full time to the Manned Spaceflight Center, and the surgeons would usually be on temporary loan from the Air Force or Navy. There were also two Australian flight surgeons and a few civilians who could be called. The flight surgeons were carefully selected and well trained, but they could not realistically be expected to be as intimately familiar with the Gemini spacecraft as other members of the flight controller team who had lived with the program since its conception. That fact made realistic simulation training all the more important.

These simulations were a refinement of the training I had prepared for the Mercury monitors at Langley. Now we had the whole remote site team involved, and our simulations were more sophisticated. For five days we had been isolated in this old Navy hangar at Corpus Christi, Texas. The hangar had been converted into a typical remote site, complete with the redesigned monitoring console that had replaced the one used during Project Mercury, assorted communication and instrumentation tape recorders, and a bank of computers to give the simulations realism.

Most of the doctors being trained were familiar with similar equipment used during Project Mercury. The Gemini console, however, was a completely new design. The systems engineer's console had many more gauges and displays, reflecting the complexity of the Gemini system as compared to the Mercury capsule. The surgeon's console repeated most of the systems engineer's critical environmental control displays. Because there were two crewmen to monitor, the biomedical information was duplicated.

I continued the debriefing. "I realize that you wouldn't normally be talking directly to the astronauts on air-to-ground, and particularly these two. It'll be a cold day in hell when Gus Grissom asks to talk to a flight surgeon. I also realize that systems would pick up this problem as a loss of cabin pressure as soon as you had AOS, but we are not here to train systems engineers today. We are training aeromedical flight controllers. We have a cabin pressure gauge on our console, and it's our responsibility to set the alarm limits before each pass and monitor all the life-critical parameters.

"Jack, I turned off the alarm on your cabin pressure gauge, and you didn't catch it on your pre-pass checklist. You were distracted when the astronauts asked to talk to you, and you were concentrating on making a clinical diagnosis before loss of signal. Incidentally, your voice procedures were very good; unfortunately, we just lost two more astronauts. Now, let's turn to your *Gemini Flight Controller Handbook* and go over this environmental control system diagram again."

I launched into a detailed discussion of the Gemini ECS, explaining its function and outlining the failures that could cause a loss of cabin pressure. "Now, on a mission, the surgeon and systems engineer would have seen this problem as soon as the spacecraft came over the hill and alerted Cap Com. I think the surgeon should see it first because he has fewer gauges to monitor. Cap Com's first words would probably have been: 'Gemini Three. This is Hawaii Cap Com. We have an indication of low cabin pressure. Stand by for your emergency procedures.'

"Now let's see, who's next? Bob, you're the surgeon on the good ship *Rose Knot Victor,* and this is the third pass. Here are the copies of your previous messages. We'll have AOS in five minutes . . . and Bob, don't forget your pre-pass checklist."

The last Mercury flight had been on 15 May 1963, and the first Gemini mission was not even scheduled until late in 1964. This date would almost surely slip because of the many technical problems that were developing. NASA needed to continue the momentum of public and political interest that had developed with the successful Mercury Project. Mercury had proven the feasibility of orbiting a man in a spacecraft and returning him safely to earth, but it had proven very little else. Gemini would also be an operational program with the major objectives of rendezvous and extravehicular activities (EVA) in preparation for Apollo. Research—particularly medical research—would continue to be relegated to a secondary position, and the research community was getting restless.

A plan was proposed to satisfy both of these objectives at very little increase in program cost. The idea was to add an instrumentation package to one of the unused Mercury capsules and orbit it for one or two weeks. The experiments planned for this mission would concentrate on earth resources and medical experiments. Martin Marietta Corporation was awarded the contract to determine the feasibility of the program, and the idea got as far as a design engineering inspection held at the plant near Denver. I was asked to represent Medical Operations because the plan seemed to have some merit. Several medical experiments had been proposed as part of the instrumentation package. Although the report was favorable, funding did not materialize. The only tangible result was a weekend ski trip in the Colorado Rockies.

NASA flight surgeons in Medical Operations had no problem maintaining their interest and felt no perceptible slump between the two space programs. There were enough medically related activities to both maintain their interest and keep them from feeling restless. Practically every facet of the Gemini Program required medical involvement to some degree.

The Gemini ejection seat required special attention, and because I had studied the ejection system in every jet I had flown, I was asked to provide the medical input. I had never ejected from an aircraft, but I had considered it as the best way out of several emergency situations.

I could remember the details of each of these emergencies vividly: the three fire warning lights, the two low fuel states, the various instrument failures, the nozzle failure in the F3H, and the carrier accident in the A-4. Each time I was impressed with the value of a good, reliable ejection system that could take me to safety if all other emergency measures failed.

The Gemini ejection seat was like none I had ever studied, and the design requirements on this seat were unreal. It was supposed to safely eject the crew at any time from before launch until the spacecraft had reached an altitude of 70,000 feet and an airspeed of 2.7 times the speed of sound.

I knew from my Navy experience that fifty percent of all U.S. Navy ejections over 350 knots had resulted in fatal or serious injuries. They were talking about ejecting at 70,000 feet and over five times that airspeed! It appeared that the design engineers had taken the specifications on human tolerance to the absolute limit and had designed to that limit.

The physicians in Medical Operations had serious concerns about that approach. We knew that maximum limits had little meaning in terms of individual survival in a particular escape system. We knew that the forces exerted on a pilot during an open-seat ejection were due to several factors: the accelerative forces caused by the ejection seat itself, the wind blast effect caused by the force of the wind, and the decelerative forces as the pilot, the seat, and the chute slowed from the airspeed at the time of ejection to the negligible speed of the pilot descending in a fully deployed parachute.

In order to safely separate the crew from the Gemini spacecraft and clear the danger area, a rocket and a catapult of unusual force was required. A system was developed to give about 600 feet of separation, but it would subject the pilot to a sustained acceleration force peaking at about twenty-four times the force of gravity (24G). Dr. John Paul Stapp had survived acceleration forces of forty-six times the force of gravity when he was thrown forward by braking forces in a rocket sled test in New Mexico; so 24G was considered, by the design engineers, to be well within human tolerance. The fact that the direction and duration of these forces made a difference in human survivability seemed to have escaped consideration.

The wind blast is dependent upon airspeed and altitude. It is measured in pounds per square foot (PSF) as dynamic pressure. The maximum dynamic pressure (called Max-Q) expected during the Gemini launch profile was 820 PSF. Dr. Stapp, during his sled ride, had experienced over 1000 PSF; so this was also considered to be within human tolerance.

The decelerative forces were primarily dependent upon airspeed, density of the atmosphere, and the pilot's coefficient of drag or wind resistance (which would be constantly changing). These forces were also considered to be within human tolerance when they were taken separately. The unfortunate fact was that maximum decelerative force and wind blast would be greatest early in the ejection sequence. All of these forces could be acting simultaneously.

To survive, the astronaut must remain conscious and actively hold on to prevent arm flailing; his legs must remain secured by the heel stirrups and knee straps. At altitudes above 25,000 feet, his pressure suit must be pressurized to at least 3.5 PSI before ejection and remain undamaged until he reaches an altitude where ambient air is breathable. He must then be able to consciously open his faceplate and breathe ambient air before his limited oxygen supply is exhausted.

These individual forces may have been each technically within human tolerances, but when the cumulative forces were considered from a physiological standpoint, a successful ejection from the Gemini spacecraft became highly unlikely.

From a mechanical standpoint, the ejection sequence was an engineer's nightmare; the ejection sequence was activated by an elaborate network of fuses, each burning at a predetermined rate and setting off various events in turn. It was designed to: first, open the hatches; second, fire the catapult; third, ignite the rocket motor. The sequence then continued to other events, such as seat separation, drogue chute deployment and release, and main chute deployment. Each of these events had to occur exactly on time, and each part of the system had to function exactly as designed, or there was no chance of surviving an ejection.

The seat was being tested by the Navy at the Parachute Test Facility at El Centro, California. One design requirement was an off-the-pad ejection capability. The first live firing of this system in a simulated off-the-pad ejection was carried out with anthropometric dummies while the first Gemini astronauts, Gus Grissom and John Young, watched from a safe distance.

During this test, the fuse blew by one of the seals and activated the seat ejection mechanism (steps two and three) before the hatches were completely open (step one). The obvious result was a lot of smoke and fire in the cockpit and the complete destruction of two very expensive anthropometric dummies. These two fearless astronauts managed to get off a few weak wisecracks—"Who are the real dummies who want to ride this thing?"—however, it was noted that no one was ever tempted to try the Gemini ejection seat under actual conditions. Even when Wally Schirra had a clear indication for an off-the-pad ejection (ignition followed by engine shutdown), he elected to disregard the ground rules and wait it out.

After some early, and rather spectacular, failures, the seat had been proven to function properly in a series of demanding tests before *Gemini 3* was launched. The envelope had been reduced so that ejection was the primary means of escape only up to an altitude of 15,000 feet; it was the backup mode to 50,000 feet. I was confident that the system would have resulted in a safe escape even in an off-the-pad situation, but I was just as glad the Gemini Program ended without a live ejection under actual emergency conditions.

For the Apollo Program, an escape rocket was designed that would lift the entire spacecraft off the booster if there was a failure during launch; so no ejection seat was used for Apollo. During the Apollo Program, however, an ejection system similar to the Gemini seat was credited with saving two lives—Dave Scott and Joe Algranti—in lunar landing trainer accidents.

The first shuttle also carried ejection seats for use in the event of a landing accident; they also were not used.

Another system that required some attention from Medical Operations was not a system at all—it was an operational compromise. In the initial planning stage, there was an abortive attempt to have the Gemini spacecraft land on a runway using a hang glider wing and retractable landing gear. This method was discarded early in the program in favor of parachutes and a water landing similar to the system used during Project Mercury.

————

Gus Grissom had previous experience with a water landing after his suborbital flight. It nearly cost him his life. For that mission I was on the *Rose Knot Victor*, and the ship was stationed a few miles from the planned landing site. As the RKV Surgeon, I received and monitored the telemetered electrocardiogram and respiration tracing on Gus from shortly after lift off until he had landed and disconnected the biomedical instrumentation cables. The Mercury hatch was blown prematurely; the spacecraft began to fill with seawater. Gus managed to exit the capsule and swim a short distance away, but his suit was also filling with water. Between gulps of seawater, he waved at the helicopter, trying to let someone know he was drowning. The helicopter crew thought he was signaling that he was OK. They were occupied trying to save the capsule.

They lost the Mercury capsule; then they managed to save a water-logged and very angry astronaut. No one successfully explained how the emergency-hatch jettison level was activated; it had been designed to guard against such an event. Needless to say, it was redesigned before the next flight to make it fail-safe. The same care was taken in the design of the Gemini escape system.

The Gemini spacecraft had several problems when it came to a water landing that the Mercury capsule did not have. The Mercury capsule was shorter and had a skirt attached to the heat shield that could act as a sea anchor and help stabilize the capsule after landing. Gemini was longer, thinner, and did not have a sea anchor. It had about as much stability in the water as a cola bottle. The astronauts were confident that these problems could be overcome, but they had to prove it under actual sea conditions.

They needed four- to six-foot waves for the test, and the waters of Galveston Bay were seldom that rough. This post-landing water survival test was an important part of the pre-flight checkout before the first Gemini flight, and John Young and Alan Bean, both naval aviators, were elected to work on this problem. Each of the astronauts were assigned to represent the astronaut's office in a particular phase of the program, and water survival was the responsibility of astronaut Alan Bean. Medical Operations took its cue and assigned a flight surgeon/naval aviator to monitor the test.

Finally, sea conditions were right for the test, and along with a host of observers, photographers, engineers, and technicians, I was on my way to the *Retriever*. The *Retriever* was a flat-bottomed hulk that the Navy used to use in beach landing assaults. The technical designation was *LCI*, which stood for landing craft infantry, but few reminders of its wartime duties remained. The old craft had been given a bright new coat of NASA paint and specially outfitted for survival training exercises and tests such as this one. Every square foot of deck space was taken up with special winches, lines, instrumentation cables, and other assorted equipment.

The boiler-plate Gemini capsule was on board; it could be hoisted over the side and tethered on a line that contained the instrumentation and communications cables. These lines led to the only part of the ship not already used for some, more pressing requirement—a small compartment, void of portholes, next to the large diesel generator. Into this compartment was crowded a hodgepodge of monitoring and communications equipment. The astronaut's EKG could be monitored on a small oscilloscope and an old chart recorder. Voice communications could be maintained if you could speak and hear over the roar of the generator.

The test crew boarded a chartered fishing boat at the Galveston dock. This boat, appropriately called the *Buccaneer*, had a round bottom with no keel, and from the moment we cast off from the dock it started to buck and roll violently. By the time we reached the *Retriever*, nearly everyone on board was

Astronaut Gus Grissom, in a very wet Mercury space suit, is escorted by Dr. Laning across the flight deck of the U.S.S. Randolph to the sick bay. His suit had filled with water while the helicopter crew tried, in vain, to save the Liberty Bell 7 from sinking in the Atlantic Ocean. (Courtesy NASA)

seasick. Some were too sick to even make the transfer; they returned to Galveston on the *Buccaneer*.

I had never experienced seasickness. Even on my first trip to Hawaii on the U.S. naval ship *General Morton*, when my young son Danny sat on the top bunk and hit all four bunks—including the baby's play pen—with a most disagreeable mixture of his last two meals, I had been unaffected by the chain reaction of nausea and vomiting which swept through the rest of the family.

I was one of the few who had made the transfer from the *Buccaneer* to the *Retriever* untouched by seasickness. I had to admit, it was good to get off the round-bottomed *Buccaneer* onto the relative calm of the flat-bottomed *Retriever*. Wave action on the LCI caused it to rise and fall abruptly and to slide irregularly from side to side, but there was no violent bucking and rolling. Many of the test crew failed to see much improvement when seated at the monitoring console next to the noise and fumes of a large diesel generator.

The astronauts arrived by helicopter. After the usual delay for instrumentation checkout, they were over the side and in the water. Both of them experienced some nausea but they agreed, "The Gemini spacecraft was about as seaworthy as the *Retriever*." Soon, they were quite comfortable in their new environment.

I had brought some of the injectable seasickness medication from the Gemini in-flight medical kit along on this test. It was an automatic injector that would be activated on impact and could be used by a nonmedical crewman. Unfortunately, we had never been successful in convincing one of the astronauts that they should test it.

The injector could, theoretically, be used through the space suit in an emergency. It had one-cubic-centimeter (cc) vials of morphine that could be given for severe pain; however, the recommended dose for the seasick medication was two ccs—twice the capacity of the automatic injectors. Therefore, it was necessary to tape two of these injectors together in order to get a therapeutic dose with one injection.

The astronauts were instructed to open the package and jam the proper end forcibly against his upper thigh. With this action, two needles were automatically extended, and two cubic centimeters of liquid were forced through the needles into the leg or into whichever part of his anatomy that happened to be in the way.

I had thought of trying the injectors on myself, but there was one problem: I wasn't seasick. I was probably the only person on board who wasn't seasick! In the best tradition of medical researchers who had gone before me, I consciously tried to make myself seasick. I thought this situation could be remedied by sitting at the aeromedical console next to the engine room and breathing diesel fumes.

After a while—success! With a quick dash to the railing, I, too, was feeding the fish in Galveston Bay. God! I wished I had left well enough alone. I didn't know one person could feel so miserable! I crawled back to a coil of ropes on the deck and reached for the in-flight medical kit. Just as I had instructed the astronauts, I jammed the injectors against my upper leg, right through my flight suit. Now I really wished I had left well enough alone!

Fortunately, only one of the injectors fired, but that one tore through the flesh with such vengeance that I completely forgot how miserable I had been a few moments before. I was no longer seasick, but I could not move my right leg; I didn't know that one person could have that much raw pain!

The astronauts were glad to see this item removed from the in-flight medical kit. Just like the Gemini ejection seat, none of them had any intention of using these injectors under flight conditions.

When I arrived at the small apartment on Buccaneer Drive, Jimi could read the day's events in my face. "You are seasick!" Perhaps her clue was the fact that I was still holding on to both sides of the doorway and measuring each step across the rolling, pitching entryway. That night she was awakened at intervals when I lurched across the bed, and she wondered if I wasn't taking my dedication to the space program a step too far.

———

Jimi remembered an occasion when I had taken my dedication to the Navy flight training program a step too far, and she had had no trouble reading the day's events in my face. As a thirty-year-old doctor who had been physically inactive through the rigors of medical school and the hectic years of establishing myself as a physician, I was competing in the pre-flight athletic program with a group of Marine officers ten years my junior who had spent the last two years in an intensive Marine officer training program.

This was no problem for "Super Doc" because I had always considered myself superior to any Marine officer. My ego was boosted even higher in the first time trials on the pre-flight obstacle course, when with very little effort I was able to make the required time and finish well ahead of some of my Marine friends. On the final time trial I would show the jarheads a thing or two.

When my time came to compete, I was out of the starting blocks in a flash, dashed to the eight-foot wall, and was over in a single, liquid motion; that was about all I remember of the race until I found myself crawling across the finish line on my hands and knees. I was still under the required time, but well over my previous record and considerably over the times posted by each of my Marine friends.

One of the more compassionate Marines offered to drive me home, but with superhuman effort, I managed to pull myself up to the sitting position and decline the offer. "Thanks, Don, but I have my car, and I'm meeting Jimi and the kids for dinner." When I finally arrived, Jimi knew I wasn't going to eat. I sat down heavily in the booth by my older son and looked across at Jimi. "Every time I sat up to start the car, I would pass out and have to lay back down on the seat." Jimi fed me some soup and drove me home.

The next morning, when Marine Second Lieutenant Don Fraser asked how I was feeling, my reply was a nonchalant, "I'm fine. Why?"

––––––––

The Gemini program was progressing and medical inputs were being made. The prime and backup crews took an active role in each phase of mission planning and spacecraft checkout. Although some of the engineering (and medical) personnel who thought they were in charge of various areas found this practice disruptive, it had a certain logic that couldn't be disputed. The crew who had been chosen to actually fly the mission were assigned early enough that they could monitor every phase of construction and checkout of their spacecraft, participate in all tests, exercise some control over mission ground rules, and easily know more about that spacecraft and that mission than any of the support personnel.

There were opportunities for medical inputs and requirements for medical monitoring every time the prime or backup crew was involved in a test or a checkout. There were usually three or four Gemini spacecraft in some phase of construction, checkout, or flight at all times—the flight surgeons in Medical Operations were busy.

There was also the new Mission Control Center to check out, new and revised remote monitoring sites to put into operation, mission simulations to develop and stage, and medical requirements documents to write. The list of demands on the flight surgeons assigned to Medical Operations was seemingly endless. I needn't have worried about being left out of the action when BUMED kept me on the *Lexington* for an extra year.

It was somewhat of a relief when Nig asked me if I would help check out the new monitoring station in the Canary Islands. I didn't know that this would be one of the most dangerous assignments in my entire career. The flight to the island was uneventful. With the other flight controllers, Nig and I took a TWA flight to Madrid, and after a short hop to Las Palmas, we were settled comfortably in a beach-front hotel. The new site was on the southern end of the island, twenty-two miles across a mountain road.

Ed Fendel was Cap Com and Bill Garvin rounded out the monitoring team as the systems engineer. Ed Fendel called himself the "Jewish Engineer." He and Bill Garvin had been active in developing the instrumentation network for Mercury and now were doing most of the legwork needed to check out and troubleshoot the worldwide network for the Gemini Program. Once on the site they became thoroughly professional, and Ed displayed an uncanny knowledge of engineering for one whose formal training was in business administration.

Ed and Bill worked well together and were determined to have the Canary Island station up to operational readiness in record time. That was not the dangerous part—the dangerous part was driving twenty-two miles across the mountain road twice a day.

Nig insisted on driving the rental car and was immediately transformed from a mild-mannered, thoroughly professional, Canadian physician into a fire-breathing monster. Ed Fendel was driving the other car, and he needed no transformation—he had already made his reputation as the Mad Jewish Engineer who was completely without fear and was inspired by a death wish that had, somehow, never been satisfied. Nig was actually going to try to keep up with Ed Fendel? I had faced danger before, and I had more than my share of fast driving in my dad's '49 Buick on graveled Louisiana roads. For the next two weeks, however, I would face terror like nothing I had experienced before. Nig actually did keep up with Ed, and twice each day the four of us faced and cheated death. Ed Fendel and his death wish lived on to terrorize other unsuspecting subjects at another time.

Later, Ed Fendel was Cap Com when Duane Graveline and I were sent to check out the NASA tracking ship *Rose Knot Victor* at San Juan and to participate in the simulations that would be the final test of the entire worldwide instrumentation network before *Gemini 3*. Duane had to leave to monitor a Russian spaceflight, but the checkout proceeded and the network was ready for the first operational Gemini flight. Fortunately, there were no rental cars and no mountain roads—and Nig stayed in Houston.

| 7 |

Competition

Lieutenant Commander Joe Kerwin shifted his lanky form as he spoke. "I just don't know, Fred. This scientist astronaut program may not be the way to go. I appreciate your bringing the forms over here, but I'll have to think about this."

I stopped tying my heavy flight boot and looked at my younger friend in disbelief. "Joe, you've heard me say all this before, but just think about it. Who else do they have more qualified for this than we are? God knows, I'm not looking for competition, but there aren't many of us who can pull this off. They don't require test-pilot training this time. We both know that we are not scientists, but the edge of being operational jet pilots ought to carry a lot of weight with Deke and the selection committee. We've been preselected. We know what we will do in an emergency. Almost any scientist I know would panic the first time something went wrong and would be useless to the mission, besides being downright dangerous to himself and to the rest of the crew. You know what happened to Vic Prather."

Both of us knew that Lieutenant Commander Victor Prather, Medical Corps, U.S. Navy, who was assigned to the Office of Naval Research, had participated in a successful balloon flight two years ago. He had set a world's altitude record of 113,700 feet, only to drown in Pensacola Bay when he slipped into the water while stepping from the gondola to the rescue boat. He couldn't swim.

"I don't want to influence you, but the fact that I'm a naval aviator has opened a lot of doors for me in Houston. The fact that I stayed in the Naval Reserves and still fly the A-4 on weekends gives me a credibility the other NASA flight surgeons just don't have."

"Fred, I can appreciate that, but . . ." Joe shifted his weight again, "the Navy has been good to me so far and I have a solid career outlined. You know we can't fly planes or spacecraft forever. I'm not sure that I don't want to get back into clinical medicine and start filling in the blocks for my Navy career. If I take five years out now, I'll be in the same boat that Frank Austin is; I'll have no command experience and no chance for the broad stripe."

"For Christ sakes, Joe, you are talking about a bag of peanuts, and I'm talking about the brass ring. Who the hell wants to be an admiral in the Medical Corps anyway?" I could appreciate Joe's concern. I knew I had forfeited any chance I might have had to make flag rank when I resigned my regular commission and joined the reserves so I could accept a job with NASA. I also knew that, in order to make the broad stripe, a medical officer had to fill in all the blocks. He had to have his share of sea duty, foreign service, decorations, and commendations. He had to move steadily up the chain of responsibility until he served in BUMED and commanded a naval hospital. Above all, he had to keep it clean and to not rock the boat; I had spent most of my career rocking the boat.

"Look at it this way, Joe, who else do they have? Frank is too tall, and now he's too old. He missed his chance in Mercury because he was too tall. I missed a chance at all the other selections because I didn't have the flight time and I hadn't gone to Test Pilot School. The Air Force has some candidates, like Duane Graveline, who qualify as scientists but have no flight experience. I don't know where the serious applicants will come from."

I had filed my return flight to Pensacola, then direct to New Orleans. I would cancel IFR and drop the A-4 off at Alvin Callender Field in time to catch the Navy shuttle flight back to Houston. As I closed the canopy and began taxiing to the duty runway, I could see Joe walking back to the hangar. I could almost hear what he was saying: "I just don't know about this scientist astronaut business."

As soon as I was safely up to altitude, I reflected on our conversation. Was Joe putting me on? No, we had been friends too long and had known each other too well for that. Joe had serious doubts. The obsession that drove me seemed to be absent in Joe. The same level of obsession drove every astronaut who had been selected. I knew each of them personally. I had their medical records, a copy of each one's psychological profile, records of everything they had done officially, and a good knowledge of most of their unofficial activities. Each of them had a driving motivation and a strong sense of competition. Joe apparently didn't have these traits. Maybe he had his sights set on other goals, or maybe he was just cautious by nature. One thing was sure: without this all-consuming drive, he might as well not apply.

Duane Graveline—now there was a fierce competitor. He was real competition. He was firmly established as one of the leading researchers in aerospace medicine, had performed most of the basic research into the physiology of weightlessness, and was the first to use underwater simulation of weightlessness. He was now assigned by the U.S. Air Force to monitor the biological data from every spaceflight the Russians had put up. He probably knew more about the Russian space program than the Russians. In addition to all of his professional qualifications, he was young, articulate, ran three miles every day, and certainly had the motivation. I would be disappointed in the system if Duane were not selected. Duane was definitely my first choice—after me.

Had I really asked Joe where all the competition would come from? I knew too well the kind of competition we would face. It would come from colleges and universities, from residency programs, research institutions, the Army, the Navy and Air Force Schools of Aerospace Medicine. There would be line aviators with Ph.D.s in astrophysics, geology, marine biology, and in specialties I didn't even know existed. Yes, there would be plenty of competition. Maybe Joe was right by not putting all his eggs in one basket. Maybe I should think of alternatives—what if I'm not selected?

The Mississippi Gulf Coast was giving way to the marshlands of Louisiana, and I could see the mouth of the Mississippi River in the distance. I had the Naval Air Station in sight and had already canceled my instrument flight plan with the New Orleans Flight Control Center.

"Callender tower, this is Navy jet 263, ten miles east, VFR, request landing instructions."

| 8 |

Gemini

Even the cook recognized ''Doc'' when I met the *Rose Knot Victor* at Long Beach. The NASA tracking ship's position for the first Gemini flight was in the Pacific, for the first time in the Space Program. The RKV would fill the gap between Hawaii and Guymas, Mexico, and would give Mission Control nearly a complete coverage during the reentry phase of the mission. The old ship looked better than I had remembered it. Maybe the new coat of white paint or the new Gemini instrumentation had made the difference. I had unwittingly developed a strong attachment to this old bucket. It was almost like coming home.

Ed Fendel and I had checked out the new Gemini instrumentation just five months ago. Then, we were alongside the dock at San Juan. Actually, when we were not engaged in checkout procedures or simulations, we were at one of the luxury beach-front hotels with its exotic Caribbean entertainment. Now that I remember some of the details, that trip to San Juan had not been completely without danger. It is true that there were no mountain roads or fast driving, but some of the crew still tried to keep up with the Mad Jewish Engineer. This time the RKV would be miles out to sea; even if Ed Fendel had been the capsule communicator, the danger would have been minimal.

During the aeromedical flight controller briefing at Houston, Chuck Berry had said, "I know that some of you have been to these same stations before in the Mercury Project, but it's particularly important on this mission to have the entire network well covered. This is a new spacecraft. It is at least one order of magnitude more complicated than Mercury was. We don't know what will happen during reentry, and we want to be able to collect as much data as possible. Fred, you don't really mind going back to the RKV one more time, do you?"

I didn't answer directly, but I didn't mind going back to visit with old friends. The pace of life aboard ship would be a welcome change from the frantic activity I had seen since my arrival in Houston. I needed the rest and relative solitude to collect my thoughts. For the first time, I began to wonder about the wisdom of my move to Houston. Would it improve my chances of being selected as an astronaut, or would the internal politics of NASA actually decrease my chances?

I also knew that this might be my last visit to a remote site. Mission Control at the Houston Mission Operations Control Room (MOCR) was quickly becoming operational. Most of the data from five of the remote sites was already being transmitted to Houston on voice data lines, and plans were being made to control future missions completely from Houston. The consolidation of data lines and Mission Control activities in Houston would be a significant improvement in capability and efficiency, but to witness the dismantling of the remote-site flight control system that had served us so well during Project Mercury left me in a nostalgic mood. It was particularly sad to know that this might be the last time flight controllers would be deployed on the *Rose Knot Victor*.

I had met the RKV at Port Canaveral for Gus Grissom's suborbital flight. For the chimpanzee's flight, I had boarded at Antigua, spend six weeks in the middle of the Atlantic Ocean, and disembarked at San Juan. For the first manned orbital flight, Dr. Roy Kelly and I had joined the crew in Monrovia, Liberia. When John Glenn's flight was delayed, I returned home and Roy supported the mission as the only RKV surgeon. On this trip, in support of the first manned Gemini mission, we would leave Long Beach on 13 March 1965 and return nine days later. I didn't know it at this time, but I was destined to meet the RKV one more time—in Lima, Peru in support of *Gemini 4*.

The U.S.N.S. *Rose Knot Victor* was a 339-foot, 5,000-ton vessel with a full complement of eighty-eight. The ship's company included forty-four Merchant Marine seamen and officers, and there were thirty-nine technicians on board to maintain the electronic equipment. The ship's top speed was ten knots; it was definitely not the most comfortable vessel in a rough sea. The other RKV surgeon on this mission was Captain Duane Graveline, U.S. Air Force, Medical Corps. It was good to have Duane aboard. We could compare notes on our scientist astronaut applications.

"You know, Duane, I've had more sea duty with NASA on this bucket than I had in my entire Naval career." I had been on board most of the afternoon checking the equipment with representatives from Bendix Pacific, the company that manufactured our flight controller consoles, while Duane, with his usual Air Force precision, had arrived just before sailing time. "Let me show you to our cabin; then we can go topside and watch the ship clear the port. Our room is right by the generators; so we'll have to do most of our talking out on the deck anyway."

After we took Duane's bag to the cabin and made a quick stop by the monitoring room, we returned to the deck in time to see the last line released and feel the ship move away from the pier. The time was 1600. We would be far out to sea by sunset. Dinner was the next big event in our shipboard routine, and that wouldn't be until 1730. We had plenty of time to explore the ship and talk.

"Well, Duane, I didn't have anything to do with my assignment this time. Chuck wanted someone from the office out at most of the remote sites because we haven't really exercised the whole network. I did put in a good word for you. I knew you wouldn't mind being here with me rather than off in some exotic place like Hawaii, or the Canary Islands, or maybe Canarvon, Australia. Chuck wanted his first team here. What could be better than to have two future medical astronauts at the same site?"

Duane answered with a wry grin. "Remind me to thank you for that sometime."

He continued to stare at the horizon, not seeing the passing parade of small boat marinas and seafood restaurants. As the ship carefully made its way west to clear the port of Long Beach, California, it was Duane Graveline who broke the long silence. "Fred, now what's the scoop? You're on the inside down there. Just how are the selections going? I haven't heard a word since I sent my application in except to say that they received it. They announced this thing almost a year ago. I expected some sort of an announcement by now."

I had expected this question and had my answer ready. "Well, Duane, I've purposely kept out of this because I have a vested interest. Even if I had tried to find out something,

I couldn't have gotten any information. The first cut is being made by the eggheads at the National Academy of Sciences. That has me worried. You're a bona fide, certifiable scientist, while all the work I've done has been operational research. I know that I'm what they need, but the National Academy of Sciences may not see it that way.

"I have three other things that bother me. First, I'm thirty-eight, and although they didn't put an age limit on it this time, Gilruth told me I was too old last year when I tried to get selected for the long-duration Gemini flight as a medical astronaut. Second, that damned SAT test; they didn't have that when I started college; so I went down and took the thing cold. My scores showed that I had about enough college aptitude to come in out of the rain with a little help. Third, my references worry me. I used both Chuck Berry and Deke Slayton as references. That may have been a tactical error. You know, you can hardly get those two to agree on anything. I got a call a while back from some joker at the National Academy. He said my application was not complete because he hadn't received the letter of recommendation from Chuck."

Duane looked surprised and started to respond. "Now, why do you suppose . . .?"

As Duane's thoughts trailed off, I continued: "Aw, you know, Chuck is wrapped up in his own world. When I called him about it, he was profusely apologetic and would take care of it *right now*."

I paused and studied the horizon. "I don't even know what kind of a recommendation I got from Deke. He may perceive me as being in Chuck's camp and may not put his heart into my recommendation. A lukewarm response from either of these guys could put me in deep trouble."

———

I remembered the first time I met Donald K. Slayton. The experimental test pilots were having their convention in Los Angeles in 1959, and Deke was defending the Mercury concept against nearly everyone else at the meeting. Scott Crossfield had presented the results of the X-15 flights and had introduced a lifting body concept that would give the pilot a real role in flying the spacecraft. Crossfield and most of his contemporaries considered the astronaut's role in Mercury little more than that of a primate passenger. Deke tried to convince them otherwise, and emphasized the part the astronauts were playing in spacecraft design and mission planning. His ace in the hole was that his program had been approved and was funded. I felt that, even though every red-blooded test pilot wanted to have complete control over his mission, there was not a one in the room, including myself, who would not have traded places with Captain Donald K. Slayton if given half a chance.

It was soon after this that I was selected as a medical monitor for Project Mercury and received my preliminary training at Cape Canaveral and Langley. During this time I was able to meet all the Mercury astronauts and was impressed in varying degrees with each of them. Deke was still my favorite. I took it as a personal loss when Deke was medically grounded and removed from his scheduled Mercury flight. Twenty years later the doctors would have understood more about the irregular heartbeats and the intermittently fast heart rate. It may not have even been disqualifying. At the beginning of the space program, however, everything was new ground. The electrocardiogram was the only objective means we had to evaluate the astronaut's condition during spaceflight; a sudden rapid heart rate would have thrown the whole world into panic and would have, unnecessarily, aborted the mission.

I took Deke's grounding as a personal loss, but to Astronaut Deke Slayton it was a personal tragedy. All of his ambitions and goals were being taken from him; his whole world was crumbling. From a position on such a high plateau, with his lifetime ambition within his reach, everything was suddenly gone! It was easy to understand his profound disappointment and consuming bitterness. Who was he to blame? Why, those damned doctors, of course! Medical researchers had almost caused a delay in the whole space program by sticking needles and tubes in the chimp, Enos, and now they had grounded one of the most highly qualified of the seven Mercury astronauts! If the Astronaut Corps were to learn anything from this, the lesson was: "Don't trust those damned doctors!"

There had always been some mistrust of the medical profession among pilots, because of the inescapable fact that a pilot's entire career depends on his health. Every illness, every physical examination, and every encounter with the medical profession was a very real threat to his way of life. Flight surgeons had attempted to counter this mistrust by using the philosophy that, if problems were discovered early and corrected, the pilot could avoid serious, disqualifying illnesses later on; his flying career would effectively be prolonged. This was the whole concept of preventive medicine, and it had been proven, statistically, to be correct. Those statistics, however, were little comfort to Astronaut Deke Slayton or to the rest of the Astronaut Corps. They rallied around Deke and elected him chief of the Astronaut Corps. Even if he couldn't fly, he was certainly not going to be stripped of his position as an astronaut.

Deke accepted this position reluctantly at first, but soon he even surprised his cohorts by acting like a real commanding officer of the astronaut corps. His position was enhanced when the second and third groups of astronauts were selected; he then had the seniority he needed to solidify his position. His title was changed to Director of the Flight Crew Directorate. He resigned his Air Force commission and accepted a civil service position. If he was not able to fly as an astronaut, he would make his influence felt in other ways. Deke proved to be an astute manager. Working from a power base as a Mercury astronaut, which was essentially uncontested, he expanded his influence to a point where very little happened in the space program without his stamp of approval.

––––––––

My thoughts were interrupted by the ship's bells. "Two bells." I turned to Duane. "To you landlubbers, that means it is five o'clock, and we have thirty minutes before dinner. Do you want to go down to the cabin and wash up before we eat? I'll introduce you to the rest of the team."

After dinner we stopped by the flight control consoles. They were on the second deck in what used to be the number two cargo hold. The monitoring room was a large, well air-conditioned area, completely filled with electronic monitoring equipment. The console looked like something from science fiction with all the gauges, dials, cathode ray tubes, teletypes, chart recorders, and flashing, multicolored lights. For the flight controllers, there were four high-backed chairs that could be secured to the deck if the sea conditions got too rough.

I had asked the technicians to wire an eight-channel chart recorder to the medical console so we could collect a continuous record, as well as document the calibration of our newly installed cardiotach and pneumotach meters. These new instruments would display the astronaut's heart rate and respiratory rate without the need for us to count the deflections on the tracing.

I explained these modifications to Duane and reviewed the Gemini bioinstrumentation system. "You know, we have a manual blood pressure measuring system on Gemini, rather than the automatic system we had on Mercury. Seems like we are progressing backwards, but that's all we could negotiate for Gemini. Both of the crewmen will have a cuff and a mike in place under their suit. They will have to mate the blood pressure bulb to the fitting in their suit and manually pump it up. This system requires a degree of cooperation from the crew, and I, frankly, don't expect it from this crew.''

Duane looked puzzled. ''Why do you say that, Fred?''

I shrugged my shoulders and studied Duane's expression. ''You probably haven't had a chance to know Gus as well as some of us have. He seems to go out of his way to be uncooperative when it comes to medical operations. You know, he and Deke have always been very close. I don't think he has ever forgiven the medical profession for grounding Deke; I don't think he ever will. Now that Deke is on a director's level and is making all the decisions on who is assigned to which mission, it wouldn't make much sense for him to change. Why do you think he had the honor of commanding the first Gemini flight?''

Duane still looked puzzled. ''He wouldn't deliberately fail to collect medical data with the whole world watching, would he?''

I shrugged my shoulders again. ''I don't know, but I hate to have a medical bioinstrumentation system dependent upon active crew participation. They have better things to do than pump up blood pressure cuffs.'' I was not completely satisfied with the Gemini bioinstrumentation system, but we were going to see two leads of an electrocardiogram (EKG) and respiration from both crewmen whenever they were in contact with a monitoring station. A continuous record would be on the onboard recorder. We would also, hopefully, receive blood pressure and oral temperature on demand.

It wasn't too many years ago that an EKG could only be obtained on a patient who was completely still and in a specially grounded bed. Now we were going to see a good-quality electrocardiographic tracing transmitted from an active astronaut in spaceflight. These improvements—as remarkable as they were—were started long before the space program.

As early as 1949, Captain Norman Barr, another flight surgeon/naval aviator, had demonstrated long-range data transmission, and in 1956 he had been able to monitor the electrocardiogram of balloon pilots during high-altitude flights. When I started working in bioinstrumentation at the Naval Missile Center in 1959, I found that the limiting factor in getting good records on an active subject was the electrode design. My bioengineer, Cliff Phipps, and I began working on this problem. We developed and patented a floating electrode that would minimize motion artifacts. It would give a good clinical-quality electrocardiogram and electroencephalogram on subjects who were actively exercising, or even flying operational and test flights in high-performance Navy jets. A similar system had been used since early in Project Mercury, and excellent electrocardiograms had been received. I was confident that we would receive good-quality EKGs during this flight.

Respiration was being measured by an impedance pneumograph. This relatively simple instrument measured the changes in resistance as the chest expanded and contracted with each breath. The pneumograph was reliable enough to give fairly accurate respiratory rates, but the system was subject to artifacts and could not be calibrated to show the depth of respiration.

The blood pressure measuring system was a modification of the clinical method. The astronaut had to insert the blood pressure bulb into a fitting on his space suit and inflate a standard blood pressure cuff on his upper arm. The pressure in the cuff was then transmitted to the surgeon's console, displayed on a chart recorder, and read in exactly the same way that clinical blood pressure is determined. When the pressure in the cuff was high enough to stop all blood flow in the artery under the cuff, there was no sound. As soon as the pressure was released enough to allow a small part of the blood at peak pulse pressure to pass, a sound was made as this pulse of blood hit the column of blood in the artery. The sound was picked up by the microphone and displayed on the surgeon's console. The pressure at this point represents *systolic blood pressure*. As the pressure in the cuff continued to be released at a predetermined rate, the sounds changed in character and finally disappeared when the pressure was reduced to a level where all the blood was moving freely. The pressure in the cuff at the disappearance of the sounds is recorded as *diastolic blood pressure*. All we had to do was to get John and Gus to pump up the cuff.

———

Duane interrupted my thoughts with a question. "What about John Young? I can't believe an astronaut wouldn't bust his buns to get every bit of information possible out of each flight."

I answered without looking up. "John is a good man. He's an excellent aviator—a naval aviator I might add—and he's also very perceptive and bright. He is the first one to fly outside

The second group of astronauts pose around a model of the Gemini spacecraft. Clockwise from the top right are: Frank Borman, JohnYoung, Tom Stafford, Pete Conrad, Jim McDivitt, Jim Lovell, Elliott See, Ed White, and Neil Armstrong. Two of these—Elliott See and Ed White—would lose their lives in the performance of duty. (Courtesy NASA)

76

of the Mercury astronauts, and he knows that Gus and Deke had something to do with his being selected. It may be my imagination, but he seems to walk like Gus, talk like Gus, and sometimes, he can be just as obstinate as Gus. I think they named this program right when they called it Gemini and selected these two for the first flight.''

Our discussion went on far into the night. The relaxed atmosphere aboard the RKV was just what we needed to break the tension of our regular activities and cement our friendship.

———

We would get a valid blood pressure reading from John Young during this flight, but Astronaut Gus Grissom was unable to mate the blood pressure bulb to the fitting on his space suit. Although he suspected a mechanical malfunction, none was found during the post-flight evaluation. Gus's heart rate remained slightly elevated during the mission, but was considered within normal limits and consistent with his Mercury flight experience. From a nominal pre-flight rate in the sixties, his heart rate peaked to nearly 170 during the critical parts of the mission and remained above 100 for the entire flight. John's rate, surprisingly, remained in the sixties much of the time and peaked to only 130 during reentry. To John, a naval aviator, spaceflight was no more stressful than a daytime pass around the carrier.

From a medical standpoint, *Gemini 3* had provided two additional data points—John and Gus—in the store of scientific information on man's response to spaceflight and assured us that man could be committed to longer missions aboard the Gemini spacecraft.

From a program standpoint, the flight demonstrated that the Gemini spacecraft could orbit two men and safely return them to Earth. It also proved the Gemini concept that put man into the loop and gave the astronaut more control of the spacecraft than was possible during Mercury. A major factor in the Gemini design was the use of manual sequencing and systems management; it used man's capability to diagnose failures and to take corrective action. This concept was to be proven over and over during the Gemini Program, and man was to prove over and over that he was up to the challenge.

The Gemini Program puts man into the loop and gives the astronauts more control of the spacecraft than was possible during Project Mercury. Astronauts Gus Grissom and John Young were selected as the first "twins" to fly. (Courtesy NASA)

| 9 |

Scientist Astronaut

"In October we got word from the Bureau of Naval Personnel that they were looking for scientist astronauts. It took me about one and one half seconds of deliberation before I sent in my application," said LCDR Joseph J. Kerwin, MC, USN.

I was sitting in my office alone, silently reading from a clipping I had just cut out of the *Spaceland Star*, dated July 1, 1965. The article went on to say:

> The Scientist Astronaut Program was initiated last April and, by January, 1492 letters of interest had been received. 1492—The date of discovery of a new world! Six of these 1492 were destined to become discoverers of a new world in their own right.
>
> Out of this original number, 422 were selected by the National Academy of Sciences as having met the preliminary qualifications. Finally all but sixteen were eliminated and from these, they hand picked the present six.

As I had strongly suspected, I was cut by the National Academy of Sciences. The deep disappointment was tempered by the fact that two of my best friends had been selected as the only two medical astronauts.

"I am thirty-four and one of the more senile of the group," Duane Graveline said.

Their ages ranged from twenty-eight to thirty-four. There were two physicians (Duane and Joe), three physicists, and one geologist; only two of them had previous flight training. Four others, including Duane, would complete a fifty-five-week regulation Air Force flight training program at Williams Air Force Base, Arizona. They would fly the T-37 and the T-38.

The newly selected scientist astronauts had met their first obstacle—the press conference—and had handled themselves very well. All of them, including Joe, had exuded confidence and motivation.

"The human body is a complex system. We are just beginning to learn about the functions of the body in this environment. Now we must place him in another environment," Graveline said.

"I don't know why I got the recommendation, but I know why I wanted it," said Kerwin. "We are here to broaden the spectrum of available scientific training for more rewarding experiments in the future."

I folded the clipping and placed it in my desk file. As I closed the desk drawer, the inescapable truth closed in on me: the door was closed. There was no chance, however slight, that I would be able to fulfill my ambition. Ambition? It had been more of an obsession. It had consumed most of my energies for the last six years.

Man's habitability in a new environment is in question; this is primarily an aeromedical responsibility. Lay personnel should not be required to make professional medical judgments. A medical astronaut would give insight into the program that could not be expected of a ground monitor or a lay astronaut, regardless of their training.

I had written and said these words so often that they were a part of me. My eyes fell on a document I had written four months ago. It was titled "Medical Astronaut." Deep in thought and unconscious of time or the busy world around me, I allowed my eyes to scan the pages.

. . . point to what I consider as rather serious errors which have resulted from a lack of insight into the medical aspects of the program, or the lack of a stronger medical

Dr. Duane Graveline (pictured) and Dr. Joe Kerwin were the first two physicians to be selected as astronauts. Dr. Graveline had written more than a dozen technical and scientific papers on aerospace medicine, many on the effects of prolonged weightlessness during spaceflight. He was the first to study weightlessness using underwater simulations. (Courtesy NASA)

voice in policy; I refer to the Gemini landing and recovery problems and the acceptance of an ejection seat as the method of escape in an area where the physiological stresses are not acceptable . . .

I cannot help but wonder if the chances of allowing such an alleged error to become policy would not have been significantly lessened had a medical astronaut been selected early in the program . . .

In-flight medical observations and experimentation can best be done by a physician. Even a cursory examination of history will show how few truly significant scientific discoveries have been made without the participation of one or more highly trained scientists. We may also look into history and find many discoveries which have been made as by-products of a scientific experiment. This is made possible by the flexibility gained when the scientist is actively participating in the experiment. He or she is able to pursue these tangents to successful conclusions without losing sight of the primary objectives; the immediate appreciation of observations, along with the flexibility derived from a thorough knowledge of the subject has many times produced results which otherwise would have been lost. . . The present timetable involving the use of scientist astronauts in the post lunar phase is completely acceptable to such disciplines as geology or astronomy. I feel that this timetable is much too late for the medical astronaut. Man's habitability in a new environment is still in question . . .

The problems of prolonged weightlessness and immobility resulting in fluid redistribution and cardiovascular deconditioning are problems which face us now on Gemini. These problems, along with spatial disorientation, are looming as greater threats to man's habitability now than they were after the initial Mercury flights. It is difficult to say that even these are the major problems which could threaten man's existence in space. A medical astronaut could give insight into these problems . . .

Inflight medical observations and experimentation are valid reasons to support the selection of a medical astronaut. These reasons can be explained in terms which should be relatively easy to support. There are other, more subtle reasons which are equally as important. I believe that the influence and usefulness of a medical astronaut during the pre-flight phase will be of even greater significance than his activities during orbital or even lunar flight.

In order to explore this facet, we need only to look at the profound influence aviation medicine has had on aviation during the last fifty years. While many important in-flight experiments have been performed, the great majority of our contributions have been in the areas of flight safety, personal equipment, cockpit design, survival, and crew procedures. In these areas, an understanding of man's reactions and capabilities, coupled with a thorough knowledge of the operational requirements, have proven invaluable. It is in these areas that a medical astronaut should be able to make his most significant contributions to manned spaceflight . . .

I unconsciously thumbed through the document until I came to the part on selection and training of the scientist astronaut:

The task of selecting and training a scientist astronaut is infinitely more difficult than the selection and training of his counterpart. In order to view this in perspective, we must realize that prior to his selection, the astronaut has undergone an extensive pre-selection process which has no parallel in the scientific community. The importance of this pre-selection is difficult to perceive and may not have been given its full degree of significance. It is more than simply acquiring the skill necessary to manipulate a high-performance test vehicle; we can teach the scientist this skill. But if we are attempting to make astronauts out of scientists by simply sending them to flight school, I believe our logic is completely unrealistic. Had these individuals been interested in aviation they would have entered aviation long ago. I believe that unless a person with considerable jet aviation experience is selected, jet flight training should not be attempted.

Perhaps someone had listened to some of this logic; the Scientist Astronaut Program was now a reality. There were actually two physicians in the Astronaut Corps, and these two were high on my personal list. Duane and Joe would have been my second and third choices—two out of three wasn't bad.

I knew I could never rationalize the pain and disappointment I felt at that moment; fortunately, I didn't have time to spend on it right now. *Gemini 4* had been successful. I had just finished the aeromedical report. *Gemini 5* was at the Cape. *Gemini 6* and *Gemini 7* were in the final stages of construction at McDonnell in Saint Louis. My calendar of events for July was impossible.

''Judy!'' After calling my secretary, I looked up and was

embarrassed to see her standing there. She had been there for some time, silently watching me, understanding, but not wanting to intrude on my thoughts.

She spoke first. "Dr. Kelly, which of these flights do you want to take to the Cape? And will you be able to come back here before your trip to Saint Louis?"

| 10 |

Hello Wally

Hello Wally!
You are go, Wally!
It's so nice to finally get you off the ground.

You're looking great, Wally.
Know you're late, Wally.
But you two will rendezvous before we bring you down.

You'll hear the OAMS knocking
but don't try docking,
You'll hear Tom and Frank and Jim.
They all have OAMS too!

Gosh! Oh Gee, Wally!
This is your cup of tea, Wally!
Wally, we know you'd like to stay,
But Wally, you'll fly another day,
And we'll be with you all the way!

WHITE TEAM

(OAMS - Orbital Attitude Maneuvering System)

I couldn't believe that Cap Com, Astronaut Gene Cernan, would sing this song over the loud-speaking system in the Mission Operations Control Room (MOCR). In the first place, I couldn't believe that Gene would attempt to sing. Satchmo Armstrong had a much better voice—he could carry a tune of sorts. Gene's voice wandered from word to word with the uncertainty of a camel searching for water.

Astronaut Gene Cernan was the capsule communicator, and I was the Houston surgeon on the White Team who monitored the *Gemini '76* mission during the long night hours. By this mission, we had been able to relay all of the voice and telemetry data from each of the remote sites to Houston and display the information on an elaborate maze of lights, gauges, and cathode-ray tubes so that control could be maintained from one massive room.

There was still a cap com, a surgeon and a systems engineer, but each of these flight controllers were backed up by a roomful of experts who had a wealth of data at their fingertips. The Houston surgeon had other flight surgeons and bioengineers who worked from the Mission Support Room and monitored the massive amounts of biomedical and environmental control system data that came down from the spacecraft with the persistence of monsoon in the Indian Ocean. Each of the other flight controllers had a similar roomful of experts to keep constant control of the incoming data and bring any problems to the attention of their counterparts in the MOCR.

There was also a host of bright, young engineers who monitored and directed the orbital flight dynamics. The flight dynamics officer, who was affectionately called FIDO, had to deal with changes in trajectories and other facets of the mission that I only partly understood. FIDO played a particularly important role in this mission because it was NASA's first attempt at a rendezvous of two manned vehicles in space. FIDO's other role, after establishing an orbit, was to keep the retrofire information on both spacecraft constantly updated. The mission could be terminated at any time; accordingly, the recovery officer had to keep a constant check on all possible landing sites. These requirements called for additional roomfuls of experts with computers and other support equipment.

Each of the flight controllers reported to the flight director, who reported to the mission director, who reported to the public affairs officer, who reported to the press, who reported to the world. There was some control over outgoing information, but it was difficult for anyone on the crew or in the MOCR to get a cup of coffee without the event being reported to the whole world.

I had left my seat for a cup of coffee when Gene noticed the scrap of paper on the surgeon's console. This plagiarism of "Hello Dolly" had been the product of the long hours I had spent monitoring sleeping astronauts, and it represented my attempt to keep from joining them in slumber. I was not ready to make my debut to the world as a lyricist.

At the early morning press conference, Gene and I, along with the other NASA flight controllers, filed in and found our places in front of a row of microphones placed along a long table. We faced the usual group of sleepy reporters and TV cameras. I noticed that Gene hadn't surrendered the crumpled piece of scrap paper that he had picked up at the surgeon's console. I also noticed a sly grin on the astronaut's face. I suspected the worst; I expected Gene to break out into his imitation of Satchmo Armstrong and search for the notes to "Hello Dolly." If this happened, I was prepared to deny everything or plead insanity. Fortunately, other more pressing matters occupied the press conference, and except for one short article, the medical community was saved from unwanted notoriety. The article said: "The most exciting thing that happened during the night in NASA's space program was when an unnamed surgeon got his elbow caught in a chart recorder."

The *Gemini 6* mission was to demonstrate rendezvous with the *Agena* target vehicle, but when the *Agena* did not achieve orbit, *Gemini 6* was delayed. The mission was redesignated as *Gemini 6a*, and plans were made to launch in time to rendezvous with *Gemini 7*. The dual mission would be popularly called *Gemini '76*. During the first attempted launch of *Gemini 6a*, there was an engine shutdown after ignition, and the ground rules called for an immediate ejection.

I represented Medical Operations when this ground rule was discussed. The consensus of opinion of all present was that the chance of survival was better if, when faced with engine shutdown after ignition, the astronaut promptly initiates an off-the-pad ejection. Our reasoning was simple: there may not be time enough to diagnose the cause of a malfunction before the entire spacecraft and launch pad is engulfed in a large fireball. The ejection seat is the only chance of escape; it will be effective only if it is initiated early enough. The final vote, as always, rests with the man whose life is at stake. When the final vote came, two lives were at stake.

Tom Stafford was sitting in the right seat and accepted the fact that Wally was in command. I could only surmise what went through Tom's mind during those long seconds while Wally was deciding whether to eject or not. Most of the world was holding its collective breath without fully understanding the significance of the drama. Those of us who understood the problem also held our breath. I knew the probabilities as well as Wally did at this point. We both knew that unless he chose to eject immediately there was a better than even chance that he and Tom would both disappear from the television screen in a large fireball. Wally also knew that, if he ejected, he would be using a system that had not been proven—one which had inspired very little confidence among the astronauts.

Wally was his own man; he was in command and he would make the decision. He would live or die by his decision, but Tom, at this stage of the flight, was just along for the ride. A lesser man might have been tempted to assume the command and initiate the ejection—not Tom Stafford. He was a team player; the thought never entered his mind.

Wally's decision was to not eject, and to wait it out. The result was not the expected fireball, but an engine shutdown. Wally Schirra was a hero and *Gemini 6a* was later successfully launched.

I met Tom Stafford shortly after he was selected. Jimi and I were on a house-hunting trip to Houston preparing for our move. I remember my remarks when we got back to the motel; "This guy Stafford that they selected—he sure doesn't look like an astronaut. Why, Jimi, he has less hair than any of the Kellys, and he looks *old*." (I pronounced old like it was some sort of a dread disease.) "He could be a college professor or an elder statesman, but not a fighter pilot. If they're going to select guys like that maybe I, or even Frank Austin, still have a chance." My opinion of Tom was going to change as I got to know him better. Tom was, indeed, a fighter pilot, a statesman, and many other things, including one of the most competent members of the astronaut corps.

Tom was also an excellent judge of character. He knew that if he reached for the ejection handle, Wally would break his arm. Captain Walter M. Schirra, U.S. Navy, was not the man to cross, but he had always been tolerant of Medical Operations. Wally treated medical constraints fairly and even participated to some degree in medical experiments if he could be convinced that they were not completely useless. To convince him was difficult at times, but at least he would listen. I liked Wally as a man, and there was no question about his competence as a fighter pilot; he was even a pretty fair naval aviator.

I had gotten Wally's attention two days before he was to make his first flight in the Mercury capsule. Using my medical expertise and some of NASA's sophisticated eye equipment, I removed a synthetic fiber from Wally's very red, inflamed eye. No one was able to remove the knit shirts from his wardrobe; these shirts had become an indespensable part of every Mercury astronaut. Nevertheless, I felt like I had just removed the thorn from the lion's paw and could expect some degree of appreciation. This appreciation came as a good measure of friendship over the years. Medical Operations needed friends.

The *Gemini 7* crew were friends. Frank Borman and Jim Lovell were the ideal crew for the long-duration Gemini mission. This mission was the first chance for Medical Operations to obtain a mass of good, solid data on just how well man was going to handle the many medical problems expected on a long mission. A cooperative, dedicated crew was essential if Medical Operations was to obtain the maximum information from this flight and be able to use the data to plan even longer missions.

I didn't know if either of them ever knew about the letter a young NASA flight surgeon had written to Dr. Gilruth, the director of Johnson Space Center, when the long-duration mission was first contemplated. The proposal had been a good one, even if parts of the letter could have given the impression that the writer was somewhat biased in his opinion. It pointed out, in some detail, why the pilot of *Gemini 7* should be a physician and in even more detail who this physician should be. The director's reply was not totally unexpected:

Dear Doctor Kelly:

I have studied your memorandum of October 20, 1964, in which you outline your qualifications as a Medical Astronaut. I have also discussed your qualifications with Dr. C. A. Berry and Mr. D. K. Slayton.

While we all have great respect for your ability, training and motivation, your age exceeds the current allowable value, and hence the normal avenues of selection are closed to you.

I regret this fact, but I am sure that you realize that we cannot fly people who have not been selected competitively.

Yours sincerely,

Robert R. Gilruth
Director

The *Gemini '76* mission had been picture perfect so far. The *Gemini 7* crew had accomplished most of their objectives and had opened the door to other missions of even longer duration in the future. After *Gemini 6a* was successfully launched, the complexion of the joint mission changed dramatically; it was now a mission to prove the feasibility of rendezvous in space.

For this mission, the flight dynamics (FIDO) console was augmented by one of the newer astronauts who had recently received his Ph. D. in orbital mechanics. Buzz Aldrin was a balding, sandy haired, Air Force officer who had been selected with the third group of astronauts. Buzz and his wife, Joan, lived in Nassau Bay directly behind the French provincial house that belonged to Alan and Sue Bean. The Beans lived directly across Point Lookout from the New Orleans plantation-style house that Jimi and I had built on the small, fresh-water lake in Nassau Bay.

Buzz tried to explain his theories on orbital mechanics and rendezvous, and I followed the theoretical explanation up to a point. I understood that if you opened the hatch and threw an apple forward along your orbital path, the apple would go into a higher orbit; likewise, if you threw the apple backward, it would go into a lower orbit and eventually reenter the atmosphere. How you got from one orbit to intercept and rendezvous with a spacecraft in another orbit, I would leave to Buzz and the other equally qualified FIDOs at Mission Control.

On the *Gemini '76* mission, this was exactly their problem. They had to put two spacecraft into different orbits, then determine the time, amount, and angle of thrust needed for one of them to exactly match the other's orbital position and speed. Rendezvous was one of the major objectives of the Gemini Program. The delicate procedures for orbital rendezvous had to be worked out if President Kennedy's and, now, President Johnson's goal of the "Moon in this decade" was to be realized.

NASA was committed to the lunar rendezvous method for the Apollo Program. That meant a spacecraft had to be put into orbit around the moon; then another spacecraft—the lunar excursion module (LEM)—would undock and descend to the lunar surface. Once on the lunar surface, the only way the astronauts could return to Earth was to rendezvous and dock with the command module in lunar orbit. Without the capability of rendezvous and docking, no Apollo mission could be successful.

During *Gemini '76* there was, of course, no provisions to dock the two Gemini spacecraft, but Wally felt certain that if he could rendezvous, docking would be only a technical prob-

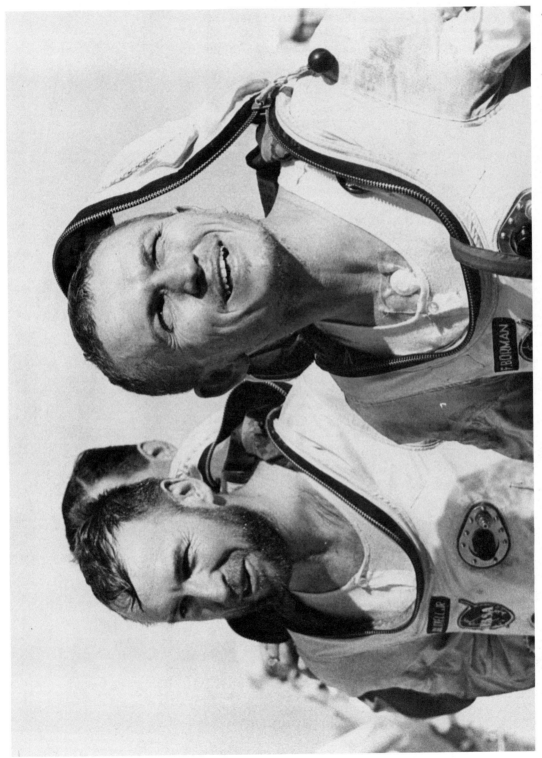

The Gemini 7 flight crew—from left to right, Astronauts Jim Lovell and Frank Borman—proved that men could function in space long enough to complete a lunar landing mission.

lem. If he could rendezvous? There was absolutely no doubt in his mind. Only those without an intimate familiarity with orbital mechanics and a thorough knowledge of the Gemini systems had doubts.

————

My thoughts had wandered back nearly eight years. Jimi and I had escorted our guest through the professional exhibits at the 1959 convention of the Aeromedical Association in Miami. "You mean that they are really going to try and put a man in orbit around the earth?"

I looked at my guest. "What do you mean, try?" Here was a man, Tom Lively, who was second only to Del Webb in the home-building industry. He had made millions through his own genius for business and, on the way, had built a multimillion-dollar company. It was incredible that such a man could doubt that the relatively simple objectives of Project Mercury could be achieved. I knew it was entirely feasible to orbit the Earth and return safely. I did not understand how a man could build a multimillion-dollar company in the home-building industry. The intricacies of big business were just as confusing to me as Project Mercury must have been to Tom Lively.

————

Mercury did fly; not only did man survive, but he became an important part of the system. General Chuck Yeager's remarks were no longer valid. The astronauts no longer had to "brush the monkey chips off the seat." To be sure, they required and received plenty of help from Mission Control and from ground-based and on-board computers, but they *were* flying the spacecraft.

Although the complexity of the Gemini systems and the requirement for real-time information demanded that they rely heavily upon computer technology, the concept of manual sequencing and system management was working. If Wally had been unable to override the ejection logic, which called for an immediate ejection when his engines shut down during the first attempted launch of *Gemini 6a*, it would have been impossible to recycle the launch in time to rendezvous with *Gemini 7*. The impact of the dual mission would have been lost; an important program objective would have been delayed.

A series of major mission objectives had been established for the Gemini Program. These objectives were directed at the investigation and demonstration of certain operational features required for the success of Apollo and future space missions. These original objectives were:

92

- Long-duration flights in excess of the requirements for a lunar landing mission.
- Rendezvous and docking of two vehicles in Earth orbit.
- The development of operational proficiency of both flight crews and ground crews.
- The conduct of experiments in space.
- Controlled land landing.

Two additional objectives had been added to the initial list of major objectives. These were:

- Extravehicular activities.
- On-board orbital navigation.

———

One objective, the controlled land landing, had been deleted, but an important aspect of this objective was retained—the active control of the reentry flight path to achieve a precise landing point.

Gus Grissom had participated in a test designed to attempt a landing of a prototype Gemini spacecraft on a runway at Edwards Air Force Base using the Regallo (hang glider) wing. This attempt resulted in structural damage to the landing gear, some damage to Gus's ego, and a decision that, although a precisely controlled landing system could be developed, time and developmental constraints dictated that this method of landing should be used later on a more sophisticated craft.

Wally Schirra and Tom Stafford had already achieved one of the program's major objectives on *Gemini '76:* they had performed a successful rendezvous with another spacecraft. Gordon Cooper and Pete Conrad, in *Gemini 5,* had demonstrated the rendezvous technique by changing to a predetermined orbit and completing a rendezvous with a phantom spacecraft, but *Gemini 7* was not a phantom. The pictures of another spacecraft taken in space were impressive; the impact on the world was undeniable.

Wally was determined to reach another objective before this flight was over: the active control of the reentry flight path in order to achieve a precise landing point. This objective was absolutely necessary if they were ever to land on a runway and gain the respect of other experimental test pilots. The fact that they still had to make their return to Earth bundled up in a package and dropped from the sky on the end of parachute lines was hard for a guy like Wally to accept.

Landing accuracy had varied from *Gemini 4* when Jim

Astronauts Wally Schirra and Tom Stafford (Gemini 6a) rendezvous with Astronauts Frank Borman and Jim Lovell (Gemini 7). The pictures of a spacecraft taken in space from another capsule are impressive. (Courtesy NASA).

Astronauts Ed White and Jim McDivitt (in the water) seal the hatches of the Gemini training spacecraft during training exercises conducted in the Gulf of Mexico prior to their flight in Gemini 4. The Gemini spacecraft was about as seaworthy as a cola bottle. (Courtesy NASA)

McDivitt and Ed White landed only 48 miles from their landing point, to Scott Carpenter's Mercury flight when he landed 250 miles downrange from the primary recovery force. Wally was determined to "thread the eye of the needle," and he proceeded to do just that by landing within seven miles of his planned landing point. Two days later Frank Borman and Jim Lovell proved it was no accident by bringing *Gemini 7* down 6.4 miles from their landing point and allowing the first visual sighting of a Gemini spacecraft returning from space on a parachute. It was now feasible to develop a spacecraft that would launch from and return to the same facility or to any other suitable landing site around the world—a giant step toward making routine spaceflight a reality.

Frank and Jim had also fulfilled another major program objective: long-duration flight in excess of the time required for a lunar landing mission. Fourteen days would do it. It was no accident that the duration of the Gemini flights were approximately doubling with each successive flight. *Gemini 4* was four days; *Gemini 5* was eight days, and now *Gemini 7* was fourteen days.

After the long-duration Gemini flight, NASA presented a midprogram review, and one of the major speakers was Dr. Charles Berry. His presentation was one of the highlights of the entire program:

> The biomedical data from *Gemini 3* through the *Gemini 7* missions support the conclusion that man is able to function physiologically and psychologically in space and can readapt to the Earth's gravity without any undue symptomatology. It also appears that man's response can be projected into the future to allow thirty-day exposure in larger spacecraft."

Chuck continued his presentation with a dramatic conclusion:

> It is difficult to realize that just two years ago, only an uncertain answer could be given to the question:" Can man's physiology sustain his performance of useful work in space? This (difficult realization) is particularly true on this great day for space medicine when man has equaled the machine!

It was perhaps an arbitrary assumption, but Chuck had said it often enough with enough conviction that the plan had

The author and Dr. Charles A. Berry, director of Medical Research and Operations at the Johnson Space Center, consult in the Houston Control Center during the Gemini Program. By 1966, most mission objectives had been met, and man had proved equal to the machine. Man could function physiologically and psychologically in space. (Courtesy NASA)

97

been accepted. It seemed to be working. The plan required the use of data procured from one mission to predict the safety of man's exposure to a mission twice as long.

The stresses on man during spaceflight are multiple, and their individual effects are difficult to isolate. We have a subject in a completely new environment, confined in a tiny capsule, restricted by a spacecraft, and strapped down by restraints. He must breathe dry, 100 percent oxygen at 5 PSI pressure; this is the pressure normally, but it will change during launch and reentry, and it will drop to 3.5 PSI during extravehicular activities (EVA) or if normal cabin pressure is lost.

He is exposed to varying cabin and suit temperatures, accelerations, and levels of illumination, as well as vibration. He will probably be dehydrated from the dry atmosphere and the diminished fluid intake, undernourished because of unappetizing food, and tired from unsuccessful attempts to sleep in such a wild environment. He must remain on center stage with the whole world watching his every move. His personal performance must be somewhere in the superhuman range; he must never appear perturbed, and all the while, he must deal with an entirely new physiological phenomenon—weightlessness.

To these stresses, the *Gemini 7* crew had to add eight distinct medical experiments. These experiments added considerably to the pre-flight and post-flight medical procedures. They also required varying amounts of crew time and crew participation during the flight. The most ambitious of these experiments required that the astronauts carefully record all food and fluid intake and output. This procedure was carried out six days before the flight, all during the flight, and for four days postflight; it resulted in over three hundred urine samples, sixty stool samples, fourteen total body perspiration samples, and a large number of diet samples. Through all of this, the *Gemini 7* crew remained perceptive and admirably cooperative. Going to the moon was going to be a piece of cake after all of this.

Before we could think about going to the moon on an Apollo mission, there were two Gemini Program objectives that still had to be met: docking with another spacecraft in orbit, and extravehicular activities. The first would be a mechanical problem and would be easily solved. The second would be more difficult.

On *Gemini 4*, Ed White had opened the hatch and briefly stepped out only long enough to demonstrate that EVA was possible. If Apollo was to be successful, astronauts must be prepared to perform useful work while completely detached from their spacecraft for prolonged periods of time. During

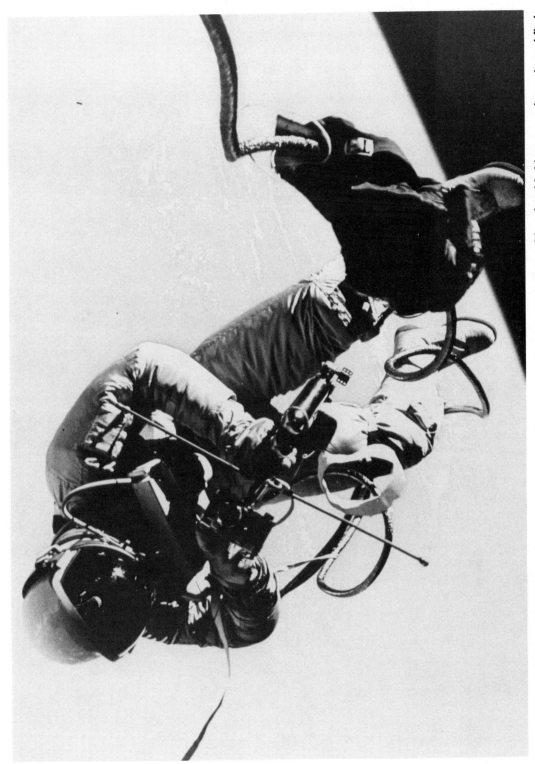

Astronaut Ed White demonstrates that extravehicular activities are feasible. He maneuvers with a hand-held maneuvering unit and finds that there is no tendency toward disorientation. However, no useful work was planned for this mission. Astronaut White had difficulty closing the Gemini hatch after his EVA. A hatch problem in Apollo 204 would have tragic results (Courtesy NASA)

Ed's brief EVA, his heart rate, which was usually in the forties, peaked to 178. How long could a man sustain this level of activity without causing significant damage to himself or causing an overload of his environmental control system?

I answered the first part of this question the next time I was at the Cape by keeping my heart rate close to 200 beats a minute for forty-five minutes while aerobically exercising on a bicycle ergometer. I knew this was more of a stunt that a legitimate piece of medical research, but it did demonstrate that the heart rate alone could not be used as an absolute limit; the heart rate could be influenced by individual variances—age, physical conditioning, psychological influences, and a host of other factors that we were just beginning to understand. After these were understood and calibrated to the individual subject, the heart rate would become an extremely useful tool in monitoring extravehicular activities.

|11|

EVA

The final Gemini pilots' news conference was being held in Houston and all eyes were on the Command Pilot of *Gemini 12*, Astronaut Jim Lovell:

> We were extremely fortunate because we turned the radar on early and had a solid lock-on at 235 miles. We were led to expect, before the flight, that this range was highly improbable, and we would have a much shorter range. You can imagine our confidence and elation as we waited for the rendezvous to take place. At the time for the terminal phase initiation for the final rendezvous, Buzz noticed that the computer wasn't giving any change in range. I looked down at the little green light that tells us we had a radar lock-on, and it was off. We just looked at each other and said: "Oh no! it can't happen to us; anybody else, or any other time, but not at this time!" Then it suddenly dawned on us that our radar had, indeed, failed!

The program objective of rendezvous had been met earlier by Wally Schirra and Tom Stafford on *Gemini '76*. Even docking had been successfully accomplished by Neil Armstrong and Dave Scott and *Gemini 8* before the thruster failure that nearly cost them their lives, but this was the last scheduled Gemini mission, and there had been no truly successful extravehicular activity in the entire program. This was the only program objective that had not been met; failure to do so would compromise the entire Apollo Program. Without a successful rendezvous on this mission, there could be no extravehicular activities—they would not meet one of the major program objectives of the Gemini Program. The radar failure could not have come at a worse time. There were manual backup methods that had been practiced, but this was not the time to find out if they really worked. The difference between success and failure of the entire Gemini Program rested on their next move. Astronaut Lovell continued his story, with every reporter in the room hanging on each word:

> We went on to the radar backup procedures which we had practiced quite a bit in pre-flight training but never really expected to use. The first thing on my list was to acquire the target visually. I looked out the window and couldn't see a thing. Buzz took out his trusty sextant, which has an eight-power scope, put it up to the window, and spotted the target. I looked up again, and the speck on my windshield turned out to be the *Agena*. So, we boresighted on the target, and the rest of the rendezvous is history.''

Buzz Aldrin chimed in to stress that this was the first and only time that the primary rendezvous had been accomplished by using the backup technique, and that the solutions they got were extremely close.

This remarkable man had pulled the rabbit out of the hat again. Edwin E. Aldrin, Jr. was thirty-five years old and a U.S. Air Force pilot with 2800 hours flight time and sixty-six combat missions in Korea. He had earned a Ph.D. in science from the Massachusetts Institute of Technology with a doctoral thesis on ''Guidance for Manned Orbital Rendezvous.'' Now he had proven, again, that when the chips are down, Buzz Aldrin is a good man to have on your team. His real test was just after this feat—he had to prove that extravehicular activities were feasible and that man could perform useful work outside of the spacecraft.

I had worked closely with each EVA on previous missions and had spend much of my time in recent months monitoring Buzz's training for *Gemini 12*. Each of the previous EVA attempts had been a part of the learning curve. Although we were confident that this important objective could be achieved, it remained for Astronaut Buzz Aldrin to pull it off.

Ed White's first EVA on *Gemini 4* had been little more than a demonstration. During his brief excursion, Ed maneuvered with a hand-held maneuvering unit (HHMU) and demonstrated there was no tendency toward disorientation, but he performed no useful work. Ed and Jim McDivitt, the command pilot on *Gemini 4*, experienced considerable difficulty closing the hatch after the EVA. Astronaut White's normally low heart rate peaked at 178 beats per minute. After this flight, the engineers redesigned the hatch-closing mechanism, while we in Medical Operations took a closer look at exercise physiology. We knew that a heart rate of 178 could be maintained for an extended time by a man in excellent physical condition without any detrimental effects. What did this mean in terms of work load?

We found that a well-conditioned man can increase his aerobic work load ten or more times for a prolonged time by exercising. Man has a remarkable ability to increase his supply of oxygen and nutrients to the working muscles without building up an oxygen debt. Unfortunately, there is no way that a limited environmental control system (ECS) can keep up with him. The ECS must supply the oxygen and remove the carbon dioxide, water, and heat produced by the astronaut. A working astronaut can overload his ECS in exactly the same way a hot summer day can overload a small room air conditioner.

The next extravehicular activity was scheduled for *Gemini 8* with Neil Armstrong as the command pilot and Dave Scott performing the EVA. Dave's primary objective on *Gemini 8* was to evaluate a complicated maze of EVA equipment. This equipment included an improved version of the hand-held maneuvering unit that Ed White had used on *Gemini 4* and an *extravehicular life support system* (ELSS), which is a chest pack with an increased reserve oxygen capacity and with greater heat removal capability than the ECS unit used by Ed. Dave also had a large backpack, called the *extravehicular support package*, that contained additional oxygen, more propellant for the maneuvering unit, and a radio for independent voice communications. During training, this equipment design proved to be more complicated, and the operating procedures more complex, than desired. Dave, however, had worked hard in the pre-flight simulations; he was confident that he could make the system work. The launch proceeded on schedule.

I had been at the Cape with Dave and Neil for the pre-launch medical procedures. After the launch, I returned to Houston and prepared to take my shift as Houston surgeon

Astronauts Neil Armstrong and Dave Scott are selected as the flight crew for the Gemini 8 mission—a flight that would almost cost them their lives. These two test-pilots-turned-astronauts proved that man is, perhaps, the most reliable component in the spacecraft. (Courtesy NASA)

Astronaut Dave Scott practiced with the hand-held maneuvering unit in the zero-G aircraft before his ill-fated flight in Gemini 8. Because of the emergency reentry, he was unable to complete his scheduled EVA. A truly successful EVA was not accomplished until the last flight in the Gemini Program when Astronaut Buzz Aldrin proved that, with proper training and stabilization aids, man could perform useful work outside of a space craft. (Courtesy NASA)

in the Mission Operations Control Room. First, I would take Jimi and the kids to dinner. As we headed north on State Road 3 to Houston, the news of an emergency in space came over the car radio. The kids were startled when the car spun around in the road and headed back to Mission Control. *Gemini 8* had a serious in-flight emergency that made it necessary to immediately terminate the flight. The abort was successful; they landed in the western Pacific and were plucked out of the rough seas by a Navy destroyer, the U.S.S. *Mason*. I met the crew at the Cape for their medical debriefing.

"Fred, we thought we had done everything right—everything that we knew to do—and we were still spinning out of control." Dave Scott was finishing a detailed account of their harrowing experience. Although neither crewman had suffered any ill effects from the flight, both of them were fully aware of what could have happened. They were thankful for the chance to talk about it.

The mission had gone well for a time. Twenty-seven minutes after docking with the *Agena*, the crew were powering down and doing some housekeeping chores before they turned in for their first night in space. It was dark outside. The cockpit lights were turned up; so neither of them were aware that the ship had begun to roll and yaw from side to side. Suddenly, Dave noticed an unusual movement in the attitude indicator on the instrument panel. The spacecraft, which should have been completely stable, had began to move erratically on its own—a control system failure! They were out of radio and telemetry contact with Mission Control—they were on their own—so these two experienced test pilots set about to evaluate and correct their problem.

Yaw and pitch rates did not exceed ten degrees per second, and the roll rates were not greater than thirty degrees per second until nearly fifteen minutes after the astronauts became aware of the problem. During these fifteen minutes, they kept the rates nulled to near zero and proceeded with a logical troubleshooting operation. They performed over twenty individual steps, attempting to isolate the problem, and constantly used the control handle to try to maintain some sort of control over the spacecraft.

NASA had accumulated considerable experience with the Gemini spacecraft and with its attitude control system, but this was the first time Gemini had docked with the *Agena*. It was, therefore, natural to suspect a problem with the attitude control system aboard the *Agena*. Neil and Dave had no way to know that the control system aboard the *Agena* was working overtime trying to overcome a Gemini control system failure.

They were still out of contact with Houston; *Agena* telemetry information was not available to them.

Fifteen minutes after the problem developed, they undocked from the *Agena*—a near tragic mistake. Once free of the *Agena*, the Gemini spacecraft began to roll at an ever-increasing rate, and the crew had absolutely no control with their hand controller.

As a last-ditch effort to regain control, they activated their reentry control system and opened all of the attitude control system circuit breakers. To do this, they had to reach the circuit breaker panel, located in the only place in the spacecraft not already used for vital instruments and controls. These circuit breakers were seldom used; so they had been put on a panel between the two seats on the rear bulkhead at the level of the astronaut's head. In order to even see the circuit breakers, the astronaut would have to bend forward, twist his body and turn his head to the appropriate side.

By this time the spacecraft was rolling at the rate of nearly one revolution every second. At these spin rates, any movement of the head would have caused severe disorientation, disabling nausea, and complete incapacitation. Neil and Dave knew this; they knew that their heads must be held completely still against their head rests. Only familiarity with the spacecraft and inherent, cool professionalism allowed these two test pilots turned astronauts to set the necessary circuit breakers without moving their heads. As long as they held their heads tightly against their headrest, they were able to function; the sensation was much like that experienced in a tight spin during their more conventional flying career.

After this time in their emergency, they made radio contact with the Coastal Sentry *Quebec*, but they were still too busy to talk. Their roll rate had increased to 300 degrees per second and was increasing by the second; they had no control with the hand controller. Finally, by selecting a direct control mode and by using more than half of the fuel from their primary and backup reentry control systems, they were able to stabilize the spacecraft. Control of the spacecraft was reestablished twenty-five minutes after the problem developed and ten minutes after the roll rates had exceeded thirty degrees per second. When contact was established with Houston, the spacecraft was under control, but, with most of their reentry control system fuel expended, their emergency was not over yet!

The attitude of a spacecraft must be maintained within narrow limits upon reentering the earth's atmosphere, or the craft will either skip back into space or enter at too great an angle and burn. Attitude control requires fuel; most of their fuel was gone!

During the flight of Gemini 8, a failed thruster caused the spacecraft to spin out of control at more than one revolution per second. Spinning at this speed threatened the flight crew with disorientation and complete incapacitation. Astronauts Neil Armstrong and Dave Scott were able to bring the spacecraft under control only after using most of the fuel they needed for reentry. They then made an emergency flameout reentry, landing in a rough ocean 500 miles east of Okinawa. They are shown assisted by divers and awaiting pick up by a Navy destroyer, the U.S.S. Mason. (Courtesy NASA)

In order to conserve the remaining RCS fuel, an immediate contingency landing was imperative. I knew that this was something like a precautionary flameout approach to a carrier, but these two professionals did the near impossible—they reentered the earth's atmosphere and landed safely.

I was able to conclude in my aeromedical report that "Once again we can say that, with proper selection and training, man is an extremely reliable component—perhaps the most reliable one in the spacecraft."

Mission planners had assumed that EVA missions would build in complexity, using information obtained from the previous flight on the next EVA; so the extravehicular activities planned for *Gemini 9* were even more ambitious than those planned for *Gemini 8*. Now, with the failure of *Gemini 8* to supply an important point in the learning curve, the planned EVA for *Gemini 9* would be even more difficult. On this mission the pilot was to evaluate the extravehicular life support system and the U.S. Air Force astronaut maneuvering unit (AMU), a complicated piece of space hardware straight out of "Buck Rogers."

The AMU was a back pack that included a stabilization and control system, a hydrogen peroxide propulsion system, a life support oxygen supply, and a radio for voice communications. The AMU would be stored in the adapter section of the spacecraft that connected the Gemini spacecraft to the *Titan* propulsion rocket. In order to reach the AMU, the pilot had to exit the spacecraft using the ELSS for life support, move to the adapter section, and position himself completely out of the command pilot's view. Before he could proceed with the AMU checkout, he had to disconnect himself from the spacecraft instrumentation system. Therefore, he would be unmonitored—completely on his own—for an indefinite period of time. This plan did not make any of the flight surgeons in Medical Operations feel confident, but the astronauts believed that the mission could be completed as planned.

Another tragic set of circumstances made this mission even more difficult. The original crew scheduled for *Gemini 9* was Elliott See and Charlie Bassett with Tom Stafford and Gene Cernan as backup. After Elliott See and Charlie Bassett were killed in a T-38 accident at Saint Louis, Tom and Gene became the prime crew. Tom Stafford had just flown on *Gemini '76*. He was tired. There was a heavy emotional load on both of these men. However, they were also professional test pilots, and as professionals, they set about training to make their mission work.

Just as in *Gemini 6a*, the *Agena* was lost on the first attempted launch of *Gemini 9*. Astronaut Stafford again had to find another target vehicle. Two weeks later, an augmented target adapter was launched, and after several holds, *Gemini 9* was successfully launched. Fortunately, none of these holdups were as dramatic as the *Gemini 6a* engine shutdown.

This mission proved that there was an insufficient appreciation of the difficulty associated with extravehicular activities. The assigned tasks were much more difficult than had been anticipated. Gene experienced considerable difficulty maintaining his position. He was unable to make the proper connections necessary to activate the AMU and finally had to discontinue the EVA due to a fogged visor. The task of preparing the AMU and the lack of body restraints resulted in work loads that exceeded the design limits of the ELSS. The fogged visor was attributed to Gene's high respiratory rate and to the resulting high humidity in his helmet. He was alone, exhausted, blinded by the fog in his visor, and working against the restrictions of a bulky, pressurized space suit. He was groping around the unfamiliar adapter section of the spacecraft unsure of where his next "step" would take him. Astronaut Gene Cernan was lucky to be able to find his way back to the cockpit.

For over twenty minutes while he was attempting to activate the AMU, he was disconnected from the bioinstrumentation system; we could not estimate his work load. Except for this time, we monitored his EKG during the entire EVA of over two hours and found his heart rate ranging from 130 to 180 beats per minute. The environmental life support system was not designed to handle this much body heat and moisture; the ELSS was overloaded.

If *Gemini 9* was too complicated, mission planners overcompensated on the *Gemini 10* mission. Mike Collins had only to operate the hand-held maneuvering unit. The HHMU and the ELSS were on a 50-foot umbilical line, and everything except the nitrogen propellant line for the HHMU was attached before the hatch was opened. Mike was able to transfer to the target vehicle that had been launched four months earlier for *Gemini 8* and retrieve a micrometeorite collection package. His heart rate remained between 100 and 130 until he experienced some difficulty closing the hatch; then it peaked to only 160 beats per minute.

Astronaut Collins performed all of his assigned tasks with relative ease; the mission was a complete success. During *Gemini 10*, however, the entire EVA was only slightly over thirty minutes in duration, and the mission plan did not address many of the knotty problems that gave Gene Cernan so much trouble on *Gemini 9*.

The task required of Astronaut Dick Gordon on *Gemini 11* was nearly as simple as those accomplished on the previous mission. Perhaps Astronaut Collins had just made it look simple. We were soon to find that nothing connected to spaceflight is simple. Dick's main task was to attach a 100-foot tether line between the Gemini spacecraft and the *Agena*. The equipment was the same as on *Gemini 10* except that the fifty-foot umbilical had been decreased to thirty feet to reduce storage and handling problems. The hand-held maneuvering unit was stored in the adapter section with two cameras, which were to be retrieved during the EVA.

Although the Houston Surgeon did not know it at the time, the extravehicular astronaut, Dick Gordon, had expended a considerable amount of energy connecting the ELSS before the hatch was opened. During this procedure the spacecraft had not been in contact with Mission Control, and there had been no direct transmission of biomedical data. The on-board biomedical recorder, however, was recording a heart rate of over 150 beats per minute.

Astronaut Gordon's first task after opening the hatch was to position the EVA camera. This task was accomplished with some difficulty, and his heart rate went from 110 to 150 and stayed in that range. Dick indicated then that he was tired but would continue to the nose of the spacecraft and attach the tether. To do this he only had to slip a fitting over the docking bar and tighten it with a handle, much like you would open a faucet. He had practiced this in the zero G aircraft; during the brief periods of weightlessness, he was able to float over to the nose of the mockup, straddle it like a present-day cowboy riding the bull at Gilley's, and easily perform the task.

During the mission—in real weightless conditions—each time the extravehicular astronaut tried to clamp his legs around the spacecraft in true cowboy style, he would go sailing off into space. Each time he would try to tighten the fitting, he would turn in space rather than turn the fitting. Dick became frustrated by his inability to position himself. His heart rate was approaching 170, and he was overloading his environmental control system, as well as his own physical capacity.

In Medical Operations (now called the Center Medical Office), we had effectively expanded our collective knowledge of exercise physiology. Now, the Houston Surgeon was armed with the results of pre-flight studies using a bicycle ergometer that showed the heart rate and oxygen utilization curves for each of the EVA astronauts. These data could be converted into a relatively accurate estimation of the current work load using only the subject's heart rate. Commander Richard Gordon, at

170 beats per minute, was approaching his personal maximum oxygen utilization level and was generating nearly 3500 Btu/hr of heat. The extravehicular life support system could maintain satisfactory cooling and moisture removal only when the work level was controlled so that the metabolic rates were kept at less than 2000 Btu/hr.

Houston Surgeon recommended that the extravehicular astronaut stop, relax in the neutral position of his space suit, and rest a few minutes before resuming his task. Dick was able to do so and finally managed to connect the tether. By this time he was too hot and too exhausted to continue extravehicular activities.

There was one chance left in the Gemini Program for a successful EVA. Colonel Buzz Aldrin was the man of the hour.

As early as July of 1966, scientists from the Langley Research Center had sponsored a demonstration of water emersion as an EVA simulation technique. A contractor was found who would stage the simulations in a swimming pool north of Boston, and Mike Collins was the first astronaut subject. Mike reported that body positioning problems and associated fatigue strongly resembled the conditions he had experienced in space.

I had been scuba diving since 1955 and was familiar with this brand of weightlessness; so I accompanied Buzz to Boston and prepared to monitor his biomedical functions during the simulations. In the four weeks prior to *Gemini 12*, we were able to construct a complete time line of his EVA mission and measure his heart rate during each activity.

Buzz's heart rate ranged from 80 to 120. These rates, when compared with his ergometer studies, indicated that his work load would remain well within the capabilities of the extravehicular life support system. If it did, Buzz should have no problem completing all of the EVA tasks and ensuring that the last major objective of the Gemini Program was achieved.

Astronaut Buzz Aldrin had learned well from the previous EVA missions. During *Gemini 12*, the EVA work loads were limited by design changes, operational changes, and in-flight monitoring. Dick Gordon had exhausted himself attaching the *Agena* tether; on *Gemini 12*, Buzz simply had to slip a loop over the docking bar and pull it tight. Dick experienced difficulty moving from the cockpit to the work station on the *Agena*; Buzz was equipped with a telescoping handrail that he installed during his first standup EVA. He was able to move along the handrail with little effort. Both Gene Cernan and Dick Gordon had difficulty maintaining their positions; Buzz was provided with a waist tether and portable handrails that could be pinned in nearly any position he wanted to maintain. He had handrails, foot restraints, and tether connections positioned to give him complete stability, maneuverability, and control of his body position.

It was considered unwise to attempt an evaluation of the astronaut maneuvering unit on this mission. In its place a work station was installed in the adapter section with which Buzz could evaluate various types of connectors, bolts, and tools to be used on future missions. Astronaut Aldrin's objectives were: first, to evaluate the connector or tool, and second, to evaluate the restraint system. He trained himself during the underwater simulations to perform these tasks while using a minimum amount of energy. These realistic simulations, in a swimming pool near Boston, gave him the subjective means to pace himself.

During the actual EVA, I followed Buzz's activities carefully from Mission Control and planned to advise him if his heart rate was sustained at a level approaching 140 beats per minute. This rate would have meant that he was approaching 2000 Btu/hr and was in danger of overloading his environmental control system. Such a warning was not necessary.

During the mission, his heart rate exceeded 140 only once—when he stopped to give a prepared speech to Houston and to the world. Public speaking was evidently not Colonel Aldrin's favorite pastime. Except for this speech, he seemed to be completely at ease and sure of himself.

Buzz had conditioned himself to relax completely within the neutral position of his space suit and make all movements slow and deliberate. When a small movement was adequate to perform a task, he would use only the necessary muscle group. If a restraint strap would substitute for muscle action, he would rely on the restraint system to maintain position. He was effectively in control of the situation—methodical and professional.

———

Every major objective of the Gemini Program had been finally realized, and Astronaut Edwin "Buzz" Aldrin had played a major role in at least two of them: orbital rendezvous and extravehicular activities.

| 12 |

Indestructible

"Joe, I still think the plane is a killer." The man sitting next to me on the Navy shuttle flight to New Orleans was Captain Joe Algranti. We were discussing the latest in a series of aircraft accidents involving astronauts—one that had taken the life of Astronaut C. C. Williams.

Joe Algranti was NASA's Chief Pilot at the Johnson Space Center. The name of the center had recently been changed from the descriptive title of *Manned Space Center* to one that would honor the man who had the most influence on the site selection in his home state. The honoree also happened to be the president of the United States.

At the Johnson Space Center, Joe Algranti managed a select group of administrative pilots who flew the Gulf-Stream and the helicopters, and test-flew the T-38s that were used by the astronaut corps. Joe was also the commanding officer of a reserve helicopter squadron at the Naval Air Station in New Orleans. He flew helicopters on weekends, and while I flew A-4 Skyhawks.

I continued my line of reasoning. "You know they're using the T-38 as a cross-country aircraft. It just isn't a good cross-country aircraft. Its range is much too short and it's entirely too unforgiving. They are stretching their luck every time they fly from Houston to the Cape. If they want a cross-country bird, why don't they get some T-39s or even some A-4s with wing tanks?''

Joe Algranti was not convinced. He loved to fly the T-38 and flew it every time he had a chance. It was fast and handled like a sports car. It was a great plane to fly. Joe retorted, ''Fred, you have to realize that these are hot pilots. They need something with guts to challenge their skills and keep them sharp. The T-38 is not dangerous if you handle it right.''

Indestructible! Joe Algranti had the same disease that inflicted most of the other naval aviators and astronauts. He believed he was indestructible, too!

I remembered the first time the crash bell had sounded. It was nearly three years ago, shortly after I first arrived in Houston. I had flashed my flight line pass at the guard at Ellington Air Force Base and was motioned to the crash scene. Joe Algranti was already there with several other NASA pilots. Dr. Sam Puma, a young Air Force flight surgeon on loan to NASA, was also there. Sam had heard the alarm in the hangar and had been the first to respond.

When I arrived on the crash scene, Sam looked up and told me what both of us already knew. ''Ted Freeman . . . ejected too late.'' There would be an accident board and Sam would be on it, but the story was all there: the goose feathers in the rear cockpit, the flight path from the end of the runway turning away from the housing area, the ejection seat, and the trailing parachute. Ted was in the traffic pattern at Ellington when he hit a Canadian goose. The heavy bird came through the windshield into the cockpit and into the intakes, causing both engines to flame out. He still had enough time and altitude to eject, but he turned away from the populated area and then ejected—seconds too late. The plane was just too unforgiving.

I forced myself to return from that painful memory to the present one. ''That's just it, Joe. These guys are not handling this bird right. They are executive pilots, and they are using this plane as a cross-country aircraft. It doesn't have any of the qualities you need in a cross-country aircraft. Look what happened in Saint Louis.''

Joe answered quickly, ''Fred, I wouldn't call Wally Schirra an executive pilot if I were you. OK. The thing in Saint Louis probably wouldn't have happened in a T-39, but the other two made it.''

————————

I didn't reply. I could only think of Jeannie Bassett. Jimi and I had rushed over to the corner house on our block with Sue and Alan Bean as soon as the word of the crash came. This custom had carried over from Navy and Air Force squadrons where a flight surgeon accompanied a fellow pilot to tell the surviving widow whenever there was a fatal aircraft accident. I had done this too many times during my Navy career, and the task had not gotten easier. Charlie and Jeannie Bassett were neighbors and had become close friends. I had worked closely with Astronaut Bassett in preparation for his scheduled flight and had grown to respect him as a thoroughly professional test pilot and as a close personal friend.

Charlie Bassett had collected old cars. Nearly a year before, when both our families lived in Clear Lake City, Charlie sold Danny a Model A Ford for $250.00. Charlie had spent considerable time with Danny helping him fix up the old car; between them, they had restored the Model A to a near-perfect condition. Danny felt very close to Charlie; this was going to hit him hard.

Jeannie Bassett appeared to be holding up very well. Her husband was a test pilot, and these things are supposed to happen to test pilots—but why on a simple cross-country flight?

Charlie Bassett and Elliott See were the prime crew on *Gemini 11* and were leading a two-plane flight to Saint Louis where the workers at McDonnell Aircraft Corporation was completing work on their spacecraft. Gene Cernan and Tom Stafford were the backup crew; they were flying the other T-38. The flight broke out of the overcast directly over the field in Saint Louis and attempted a tight turn to enter the traffic pattern for a visual approach. Elliott couldn't avoid the clouds, came momentarily disoriented, and lost altitude. Seconds later, the aircraft crashed into one of the McDonnell buildings. Tom and Gene, who were flying on their wing, lost the lead plane in the clouds, broke off the visual approach, and made a normal instrument approach to a safe landing.

————————

Joe was continuing with his discussion of the most recent accident; so I again forced myself to return from a painful memory. ''Fred, I don't know what happened this time to C. C.

Williams. At 38,000 feet you would think that he would have time to get out. But you know, if he had lost his power boost, his nose would head downhill in a hurry; the aircraft *is* inherently unstable. We may never know the full story about this one.''

The aircraft accident board was still trying to determine why Captain Clifton C. Williams, USMC, lost control of this T-38 at 38,000 feet on a cross-country flight from Patrick Air Force Base, Florida, to Ellington Air Force Base, Texas, and was unable to escape before it went into the ground.

''Well, Joe, I still think the plane is a killer.''

————

I was silent the rest of the trip. I thought about Astronaut William's new, pregnant bride. She was so young. She hadn't been a test pilot's wife as long as Jeannie Bassett; she wasn't used to men dying.

I also thought about Danny, He had taken Charlie's death hard, but he wouldn't talk about it. I wondered why.

My thoughts took me back six years earlier. Danny had watched, that Saturday afternoon at Point Mugu, when I had the nozzle failure in the F-3. I was flying a target mission for an air-to-air missile test. Danny, at age nine, liked to go the the biomedical lab and see all of the electronic equipment we were working with. Even at this age, he could see the heart and brain-wave tracings and understand how they were recorded in flight and played back on the laboratory equipment. Because this was Saturday and Cliff Phipps, our bioengineer, was at home, there would be no bioinstrumentation on this flight. Danny still wanted to watch; so I left him with the missile test conductor while I went to pre-flight the aircraft.

During my pre-flight inspection, I found a mechanical defect on the F9F-6K Cougar that was scheduled for the flight; so I switched to an F3H Demon and proceeded with the mission. I was to find that this aircraft also had a mechanical defect—one that could not be discovered on a pre-flight inspection.

I called ''nozzle failure'' when I was still on the runway—too late for a successful abort. The heavy jet was soon climbing in afterburner, but its instruments confirmed my earlier impression—the nozzle had failed when it was in the wide-open position. In the F3H, a nozzle failure is like taking the nozzle off a water hose: the water still comes out, but it has lost most of its force. The Demon could still climb with the afterburner on; without the afterburner, it would drop at about 2,000 feet every minute, even on full power.

There were two ways to handle this emergency. First, you could shut down the afterburner and make a flameout type of approach, saving the afterburner for a possible wave off. Second, you could throw a switch near the throttle that would allow you to modulate, or *throttle*, the afterburner. The second method was preferred because you could make a near-normal approach. However, if you chose this method, you were using fuel at such a rapid rate you only had enough for one pass from the time that you had burned down to landing weight until you were dry. I elected to use the second option and made an uneventful landing.

Danny had been invited into the control tower to watch the air-to-air missile test; instead, he had watched and felt the tension of an emergency flight, which even at age nine, he could fully comprehend. Later, at Jacksonville, he was the first to receive the premature word about my carrier accident from one of his friends at church, "Your dad just crashed on a carrier!"

I had wanted to break the news of Charlie's death to Danny, but he already knew. "Charlie Bassett just crashed!" Danny had become increasingly more distant. He had sold the Model A Ford and bought an organ that he played in a rock group. Although the band did not play my favorite type of music, they were pretty good. Jimi and I had taken the three young Kellys to hear the Beatles concert when the group was in Houston. We were surprised that we actually liked most of the music. The reaction and response of the audience was more of a surprise. I had heard of Beatlemania, but I had never experienced anything like this. Youth was writing its own music history and it was spelled l-o-u-d!

The New Orleans style house on Point Lookout Drive in Nassau Bay was built with this in mind—it was spelled b-i-g; the entire downstairs living area was devoted to the two boys. Besides the two bedrooms and bath, there was a family room and a gym that was converted into a practice room for Danny's rock group. From the master bedroom, we could only hear a faint thump-thump with the rhythmic beat of the music. Danny and his group could practice for hours, and no one had reason to complain.

Jimi and I had designed and acted as general contractors on this house. We secured an interim loan from a local bank with the help of Alan Shepard and a final loan commitment with the help of Tom Lively. We were overcommitted and we knew it. During the final stags of construction, it looked as if the interim loan would be due before we could complete enough of the house to close on the final loan. If this happened, we would loss everything. By doing most of the finishing ourselves and cutting cost wherever possible, we were able to complete the house and close on the loan. No one, not even the three young Kellys, knew how close we were to the brink. I wondered how many other residents of Nassau Bay were as overcommitted as we were.

The new residents of the Clear Lake area were cut from a single mold. They were astronauts, engineers, physicians, scientists—all intent on the one goal of space exploration. They were, to a man and woman, overachievers. Some were brilliant; all were intensely motivated to make their mark on history.

The school district reflected this tendency. The students in the Clear Lake School District were also brilliant. They were overachievers, and they constantly scored highest in the state on achievement tests. The three Kellys had no trouble keeping up with their classmates. Danny, especially, was going to finish near the top of his class.

The students in the Clear Lake School District were also restless, and they were vulnerable. The sixties were a time of restless youth throughout the United States; it was a time of loud music, protest, and drug experimentation. These three signs of the times did not necessarily go together—it just seemed that way. The war and the military were the prime targets of the protest, but the semimilitary environment of the space program, the church, the school, and the establishment, in general, were not far behind.

It was almost expected that the youth of the Clear Lake would again lead the field. Most of the men were away a large part of the time; they were totally involved in their work. The mothers were involved in the thousand and one things that are inherent to a growing, affluent community. Danny's grades began to drop, and his interest in my work had disappeared. I was worried.

The telephone call came after Jimi and I were asleep. I didn't catch the officer's name, but the rest of the opening comment jolted me into awareness: "We have your two sons down here at the station and would like you to come down and pick up your youngest son, Dewey. We may have to keep your oldest son overnight for further questioning."

I knew that the band was trying out for a new engagement that night, and 15-year-old Dewey had gone along to listen. I had also noticed some new amplifiers and speakers that some of the band members had left in the practice room. I wished I could buy Danny a better organ, but at present, that was completely out of the question.

As the full story unfolded over the next several days, it was apparent that Danny had taken the financial matters into his own hands. On three different nights, Danny had rolled the old Volkswagen bus out of the driveway, pushed it down the street before starting it (so he would not awaken anyone), then picked up the other members of the band. After two unsuccessful attempts, they raided an electronic supply house on the other side of Houston and took over $1700 worth of musical equipment.

On at least one of the unsuccessful attempts, the owner was sitting behind the door with a loaded shotgun in his lap. Although it didn't come out in the hearings, Danny and his friends were also armed. The owner, after a tip, had recognized his equipment on the stage, and the arrest was made. The owner agreed not to press charges provided we would make complete restitution for any equipment that could not be returned. The district attorney approved, and Jimi and I felt thankful that the problem had been caught early enough and corrected without nearly as much trauma as there could have been. What if one of the earlier attempts had been successful? On the attempt when Danny had heard "something" and made a hasty retreat, the "something" was more than likely the owner with his loaded shotgun! Danny was overtly repentant and would abide by the house rules. The storm was over, but I still worried.

Although Danny's grades did not improve, he was graduated with the Class of '67, and a graduation party was held at our large, house on Point Lookout Drive. Music, dancing, and happy sounds throughout the night ended with breakfast for the entire class. Jimi, who had never been able to fry an egg without breaking the yolk, cracked twelve dozen without breaking the first yolk; then she scrambled them. There was no evidence of drugs, alcohol, or anything except normal, happy, teenage activity. Perhaps the storm *was* over.

Other families were not so lucky. In Danny's graduation class of less than 100, seven normal, healthy students had met violent deaths. Some of these were related to automobiles; some might have been related to alcohol; some of them might have been related to drug experimentation, but we would never know. There seemed to be no common thread to link most of these tragedies except their location—near the NASA Space Center.

What effect would the very proximity of so many personal tragedies, even if they were unrelated, have on Danny and his contemporaries? Would it harden them and make them discard the traditional values in life that their parents had tried to teach? They had seen the best and the most innocent of their number snatched from them. They had seen heroes die through no fault of their own. Did it really matter? Was life worth the struggle? Why work for a goal that you might not achieve through no fault of your own? Why try?

Indestructible? That was a bad joke; it was a tragic joke. The younger generation had learned quickly that no one was indestructible. For the older generation, the learning process was slower, but the cloak of indestructibility was beginning to show signs of wear.

| 13 |

Fire in the Cockpit

"Fire in the cockpit! We've got a bad fire in here!"

Every eye in the Launch Control Room at Cape Canaveral turned to the TV monitors in paralyzing disbelief. I glanced back at my medical console and saw a flurry of activity, then nothing! I turned to the bank of TV monitors. On one I could see flames coming from around the spacecraft; on the monitor that usually shows the hatch, I could see only dense smoke. The control room had been so quiet moments before; now, it was a scene of frantic activity. Everyone was looking for the scrap of evidence to contradict the words we had just heard—there was none.

I looked to the VIP section and spotted Deke Slayton. He was moving onto the floor of the control room with the same expression of disbelief and pain I could see throughout the room. Our eyes met and Deke spoke first: "You'd better go on up there."

I nodded in agreement. "You know what I'll find." Whether Deke heard or didn't want to hear, there was no response. There was no need for one. I was transported to the pad and then to the first Apollo spacecraft.

The white room provided access to the spacecraft; normally spotless, it was now filled with dense, black smoke. Firemen were bringing blowers, and technicians had already succeeded in opening the hatch. I knelt and partially entered the open hatch. A quick check confirmed what I had known—there was no chance for resuscitation.

"It'll take hours to get them loose. Everything is stuck together." I was talking to no one in particular. "I think we'd better clear the pad until the escape rocket is safe, and we'll want to get the photographers in before we move anything so the accident board will have something to work with."

I turned to the Pan Am doctor who had responded with the ambulance. "Dr. Gallagher, you may as well go on back and see that the rescue workers are taken care of. We will need three ambulances later on."

I asked for a telephone, called Deke, told him what we had found, and expressed my concern about the escape rockets. If they blew, no one on the pad would be safe. "Let's not turn this into more of a disaster than it already is—and Deke, you may want to get some photographers up here before we start removal. I'll go ahead and call Chuck."

Deke responded automatically: "OK—yeah, I guess you'd better," and the chief of the astronaut corps slowly hung up the telephone. While we were talking, I remembered that Deke Slayton had wanted to observe this test from inside the capsule. He could have done so only by lying down on the floor of the spacecraft. Better judgment prevailed and he elected to observe from the VIP room. I wondered if this chilling thought had crossed Deke's consciousness—yet.

I also remembered a position paper that Nig Coons and I had worked on concerning the 100 percent oxygen atmosphere in Apollo. The final version had omitted our reference to the danger of fire.

I was able to get a line through to Dr. Charles A. Berry, director for Medical Research and Operations in Houston, without the usual delay. After some initial comments, Chuck picked up the conversation, "Nig is already over at the White's, and Duane Catterson is going to the Grissom's. I'll get someone over to Martha Chaffee's." Chuck and Deke worked well together when the chips were really down.

" . . . and Fred, I'll get the pathologist from AFIP down there on the first plane. I'd suggest you use the BOSU. You can have better security there. I guess you'd better plan to stay for a while; you'll do the investigation." I hadn't thought of leaving, but I liked the way Chuck could make decisions when he had to.

Chuck had ended the conversation with some personal inquiries on how the rest of the staff and I were holding up and

Astronauts, from left to right, Ed White, Gus Grissom, and Roger Chaffee are selected for the first flight in the Apollo Program. A routine pre-flight test ended in a tragic disaster that took the lives of these three dedicated professionals. However, their spirit remains indestructible. (Courtesy NASA).

a promise to give my wife any information he could. ''I'll call Jimi when I get a chance.''

I had gone into some detail with Chuck on the relative positions and the general conditions inside the spacecraft. Much more would come out of the investigation, but both of us knew what happens to any spark or flame in the presence of 100 percent oxygen. I remembered using a cutting torch when I welded in a shipyard. I knew that you could cut through almost any metal with a flame if you added 100 percent oxygen. The entire Apollo spacecraft was full of 100 percent oxygen. Because this was a pressure check of spacecraft integrity, the oxygen pressure was greater than normal atmospheric pressure—all it needed was a flame.

''Hello Jimi. Yes, I'm OK. I guess you've heard the news.'' I tried to sound confident and under control. Now it was Jimi who picked up the conversation.

''I'm going over to Martha's with Sue and Alan Bean as soon as I get some snacks together. I think Gene Cernan and Barb are there already; I don't know who else. I guess you'll be there for a while. I'll find a way to send you some clothes. I know you'll be busy, but try to call when you can. Love ya.''

There was so much more that could have been said, but each of us knew what had to be done, and we both knew it was not going to be easy. Jimi had become proficient at her task; she could be depended on to be a stabilizing influence. It had helped Jeannie Bassett to know that someone outside of the astronaut wives understood her grief and felt some of her loss. I knew it had been an emotional drain on Jimi because of the special relationship we had with Charlie and Jeannie Bassett.

We had developed the same type of relationship with Roger and Martha Chaffee. Jimi had often remarked how Roger and Martha complemented each other. If any of the latest group of astronauts had the ''John Glenn-straight arrow'' personality, it was Roger. Both he and Martha seemed too perfect to be believable; yet they were genuine and sincere. There was no acting; they were really that good. Tonight was going to be hard on Jimi; it was going to be infinitely harder on Martha Chaffee. I wished I could help, but my night was just beginning, too. By the calendar, the accident investigation would take nearly two long months, but this dark night would be with me much longer.

The Bioastronautics Operational Support Unit (BOSU) was built by the Air Force on Cape Canaveral Air Force Station as a three-man hospital to support manned spaceflight. It would have been possible to do the pre-flight and some of the post-flight medical tests here and consolidate medical support in one location. However, that plan did not fit into NASA's operational plans; so the building was modified into a dispensary. The U.S. Air Force had contracted with Pan American World Airways to operate the dispensary as an occupational medicine and environmental health clinic, and Colonel Frederick Frese, U.S. Air Force, Medical Corps, was in charge of the unit. Tonight he had put his entire staff at NASA's disposal.

Chuck was as good as his word. The team from the Armed Forces Institute of Pathology (AFIP) arrived the next morning with their fly-away kits of equipment developed for the investigation of aircraft disasters. The next fourteen hours would remain a blur in my memory. I worked automatically and methodically, ensuring that the suit technicians, the photographers, and the other necessary personnel were available; supporting the pathologists; insisting on detailed notes; rechecking every item. It helped to be busy with the work at hand, but it was impossible to completely detach myself from the reality of the situation. I had worked with these three men too long. I knew them too well.

The accident investigation board had been formed with Dr. Floyd Thompson, the director of NASA's Langley Research Center, as its head. I would head the Medical Panel. I had been on more Navy and Air Force aircraft accident boards than I wanted to remember, but this was unlike any accident investigation I had seen. There were eight board members, a council, an advisory group of six representatives and seven consultants, and twenty-one panels. Hundreds of specially selected individuals from all disciplines would work on the investigation for the next two months. The final report would fill several volumes; the medical panel's report alone would be book length. The impact of the final report would be felt nationwide.

The AFIP pathologists had completed their initial work by 0100 and met with me to complete the paperwork and review the preliminary findings. Doctor Thompson, the chairman of the 204 Accident Investigation Board, had sent a message requesting that I meet with the entire board as soon as I could. I would do so in the morning; now I had many details to check, an overall plan to formulate, and detailed instructions for the other medical panel members to work out.

It had been over forty hours since I had slept, and it would likely be another eight to twelve hours before I could return to the motel for any real rest. After the AFIP team left, I layed down on an examination table and closed my eyes for the first time in two days. I could force myself to relax, but my mind would not be still. I was able to handle the events of the last forty hours, but my last encounter with Gus Grissom kept rising to my consciousness. Why did I have to think about that now?

———

That incident had happened several weeks ago. The Apollo 204 crew were engaged in an altitude chamber test, and the requirement for a pre-entry physical examination had inadvertently been omitted from the documentation. Gus was not going to submit to the examination. I was not involved; I was at the Cape for an entirely different reason. Soon, inevitably, I was drawn into the controversy. Gus would have to call Deke; Deke would have to call Chuck Berry (now director for Medical Research and Operations); and Deke and Chuck would have to work it out at the directors' level before Gus would submit to a five-minute physical examination. I asked to speak with Gus in private and was able to restore some degree of peace. Gus could be reasonable if you used the right words.

———

''Dr. Kelly, you have a call. It's Mr. Geer, from the accident board.''

I had been asleep nearly forty-five minutes and felt surprisingly rested. ''Yes Sir, 0900, I can be there, thank you.'' Bart Geer was calling for Dr. Thompson and had set up a meeting with the members of the accident board. There had been an indication of increased suit oxygen flow forty-two seconds before the verbal warning had been heard; at the same time, Ed White's heart rate had nearly doubled. The board was trying to fix the time of onset of the emergency at forty-two seconds before Astronaut Chaffee gave the warning.

I examined the EKG records and confirmed that Ed's heart rate had doubled well before the emergency, but the engineer had misinterpreted the rates; he had assumed, because the rate was so slow, that the chart recorder speed had been set at fifty millimeters per second instead of the normal twenty-five. He had, therefore, interpreted the heart rate as increasing from sixty to one hundred and twenty beats per minute, which would undoubtedly have indicated a significant increase in activity.

I knew that Ed White's resting heart rate was normally in the thirties due to his superb physical condition. His rate had increased from thirty to sixty beats per minute. This indicated that he had, perhaps, shifted his position, but it did not indicate that he had become aware of an emergency situation. At 6:31:04 P.M. Eastern Standard Time, there was a marked increase in his activity; at this time Astronaut Ed White first became aware of the emergency.

This report was presented to the board, along with the preliminary findings of the medical panel—that the burns were in each case considered survivable, but the toxic gasses produced by the fire were not. The preliminary report was confirmed later by biochemical studies. Before the final report would be submitted, I would know much more about the medically related factors in this accident. My work was just beginning.

The Apollo spacecraft that would deliver Neil Armstrong, Buzz Aldrin, and Mike Collins to a lunar orbit was a much different spacecraft from the one involved in the Apollo 204 fire. New flammability requirements were adopted for all nonmetallic and metallic materials; new standards were adopted for all electrical cables and circuits; aluminum oxygen lines were replaced with steel lines; all joints were brazed or welded; the spacecraft hatch was redesigned; emergency egress procedures were revised—the list of changes went on.

Apollo would continue to use the five PSI, 100 percent oxygen atmosphere while in space. During pre-launch operations, however, a special provision was adopted to ensure that the set of circumstances leading to this accident did not recur. The pre-launch atmosphere would be changed to a 70/30 ratio of oxygen to nitrogen. This atmosphere would decrease the danger of fire at normal atmospheric pressure and during spacecraft integrity testing.

Even after an exhaustive, detailed search, the exact source of the spark would not be conclusively proven. However, many possible sources were corrected, whether they were considered a probable cause of the accident or not. The Apollo Program would be completed without a repeat of this disaster.

NASA and everyone associated with this investigation learned much from this tragic accident, but the price of the knowledge was much too high. Why not be perceptive enough to prevent accidents like this before they occur? The new Apollo spacecraft was different from the one involved in this accident in many ways—design, materials, procedures—but no new technology was involved. The same technology was still being used on the Apollo Program; the same workers were at the same jobs; there had been no breakthroughs. Each of these changes could have been made before the accident—but they were not.

This sad sequence of events has been an inherent part of aviation history since the first hot air balloon flight; changes are made *after* accidents occur. Why not *before*? Is it economics? Certainly the changes to the Apollo spacecraft would be expensive. Is it expedience? This fire had set the Apollo Program back over a year. Is it human nature to accept status quo as the norm?

None of these answers were good enough. Accidents should not be allowed to happen. Dangers should be anticipated and corrected before they become a tragedy. Why hadn't I reviewed the emergency egress procedures for the Apollo spacecraft? I had been much closer to Mercury and Gemini than to Apollo. I was now assigned to follow the plans for Skylab; I had never even been inside the Apollo spacecraft before that tragic night.

Could I, as an Apollo crewman or even as a flight surgeon, have accepted a hatch that could not be opened with one single, easy action? The Mercury capsule and the Gemini spacecraft both had explosive hatches that could be opened in seconds. The engineering problem in Apollo was complicated by a protective shield that was required because of the powerful escape rockets—but impossible? No.

There was evident that Astronaut Ed White had gotten out of his seat, turned around, and wrestled with the Apollo escape hatch for a least sixteen long and frantic seconds before he was overcome. Could he had been saved by a quick-opening hatch? Could Gus? Could Roger? Perhaps.

There was no way that anyone could answer these agonizing questions. Everyone involved in this investigation would pledge, personally, to try to prevent a recurrence. We would, to a man, do everything possible to ensure that there would be no more accidents in the Space Program, but each of us knew there would be others.

It was nearly a month later when I was able to make my first visit to Houston since the accident. Jimi picked me up at Hobby Airport and said, "Martha wanted to see you when you got in. Do you want to stop on our way home?" She read the expression on my face. "It's OK. She's at home now and taking it better than you are, I suspect."

The small, fragile girl met me at the door. "Fred, I just wanted to thank you. I know it wasn't easy."

I had come to console her, but—for a long moment—all I could do was hold on. When I regained some of my composure and could speak, I looked into her eyes and managed to whisper, "It was quick, and—I believe—painless."

There must have been more I could say to relieve some of her pain, but no words came. As I held her, all I could think of was Roger. Roger Chaffee had not moved from his seat. He would normally have been the last one to exit the spacecraft in an emergency egress. He was waiting, patiently, for his turn to exit the spacecraft—a turn that never came.

The uneven distribution of carbon monoxide reported in the biochemical evaluation indicated that his heart had stopped abruptly when the high levels of carbon monoxide reached the coronary vessels. Consciousness was lost within fifteen to thirty seconds after the first suit failed. Chances of resuscitation decrease rapidly with such extreme levels of carbon monoxide in the blood. The Apollo hatch was opened a little over five minutes after the accident by the pad crew who had been forced back repeatedly by the intense heat and the dense, black smoke.

"Martha, there was no chance for resuscitation."

|14|

One Small Step

"One small step for man; one giant step for mankind."

These words had just cracked across the miles and electrified the world with their importance when the only radio station on the small Pacific island began to play recorded Guamanian music. Jimi and I stopped and stared at each other in disbelief. A man had just stepped onto the surface of the moon and was sharing his experience with the world. This adventure was being preempted by recorded music?

I turned the portable radio off and looked around the fairgrounds. Most of these present had not even heard the announcement. It was the 21st of July, 1969; on this day, 25 years earlier, the U.S. Marines had liberated Guam from the Japanese. This was Liberation Day, the island's most celebrated holiday; nothing was going to interrupt this celebration.

The people of this small island were instilled with an intense national pride. They were Americans; their island had been an American territory since 1898. To me, it seemed absurdly inconsistent that a people who were so intensely proud of being Americans would not be hanging onto every word from the *Apollo 11* crew. This was one of the great moments in history for all Americans. An American had landed on the surface of the moon and was sharing the excitement of his exploration with the entire world. Was the remembrance of an event that had happened 25 years ago more important than witnessing history being made?

I stopped again and looked around the fairgrounds. I looked at the Guamanian people—their faces, the large families with island food spread out in fiesta style. Today was the culmination of a weeklong celebration with parades and fiestas in every village on the island. Now, in the principal city of Agana, near Asan Beach were 36,933 U.S. Marines from the Third Division had landed 25 years ago to the day, a celebration was in progress that was not to be shared with any current event. Many of those present were also here 25 years ago. The occupation and liberation of their homeland was indelibly imprinted in their memory with the blood of their loved ones and the remembrance of personal suffering and triumph. How could an event that was happening over 200,000 miles away possibly hope to compete with such a memory?

————

The small step I made, deciding to resume my Navy career, had also been a giant one for the Kellys. I had finally accepted the fact that I would never be selected as an astronaut, and it was time to reevaluate where I was going with my life. I had been a part of the most exciting program any nation had ever attempted. What did NASA have for an encore?

I had stayed in the Naval reserve, and my promotions had not lagged. I could expect my fourth stripe as a Navy captain if I returned to active duty. I had given NASA the best of nearly five years and was proud of whatever contribution I had been able to make to the nation's space effort. Now it was time to move on. I had also invested most of my life in the Navy. I enjoyed Navy life, particularly naval aviation. Although NASA had not seen the advantage of using my skills as a naval aviator, if I returned to active Navy duty I would be assigned as a flight surgeon/naval aviator. I would fly. This was the right decision—the way to go. I had only to request a return to active duty in the U.S. Navy.

In the spring of 1968, with this decision behind me, I made the trip to the Bureau of Medicine and Surgery, as I had done many times before. BUMED was located on the old Naval Observatory grounds in Washington, D.C. When I surveyed the ancient wooden and stone structures, I thought, Why don't they tear down all of these old buildings and put up an adequate office building? As I climbed the long hill and entered the building that had housed Code 5 (Aviation Medicine) as

Astronaut Buzz Aldrin walks on the moon. The spaceship that brought Astronauts Neil Armstrong, Buzz Aldrin, and Mike Collins into orbit around the moon was much different from Apollo 204. We learned much from that tragic accident, but the cost was too high. (Courtesy NASA)

long as I could remember, I had to admit, It has a certain charm. Under my breath I conceded, This is very typical. As long as BUMED is not going to change, there is little point in building modern quarters.

I turned right at the entrance foyer and entered the Code 5 detail office where Captain Cleve Hunley was sitting behind a large desk. Captain Hunley's primary function was to assign flight surgeons and advise the Surgeon General on matters concerning aviation medicine.

When I walked into the room, Captain Hunley looked up from his desk and greeted me rather indifferently, "So you want to get back in the Navy." There was no use explaining to the captain that I had never really left the Navy. I had stayed active in the Naval Reserves and had remained current in the A-4. I had been more active in my Navy specialty than I was as Senior Medical Officer on the *Lexington*. Although I resigned my regular Navy commission over four years ago, I promptly accepted a similar commission in the Naval Reserves.

"This letter you wrote when you resigned was pretty strong. What makes you think you can get along with the Navy any better now than you could when you left?"

I tried to explain that I had never had any trouble getting along with the Navy. This was mostly true. I had resigned because I could pursue my personal goals better, at the time, by working in the NASA Space Program.

"Oh yeah, you wanted to be an astronaut. Why didn't you make it?"

I felt my hair rising on the back of my neck and knew my face was getting flushed. I had come to see what billets were available. I hadn't come for a ration of—No! I was not going to let Cleve Hunley get to me. I forced a calm answer, "I had a lot of competition."

Captain Hunley looked over the top of this half-frame glasses. "I guess that makes you a loser, doesn't it?"

Now he had gone too far! Who did he think he was? What did he know about winners or losers? All he had ever done was sit behind a desk. He had never tried. I felt the tide of anger rise again, and—illegitimus non corborundum—with an unaccustomed measure of self control, I forced it down once more. I stepped back from the desk and calmly stroked my chin. "I never thought of it that way, but I guess you're right. I may be a loser, but I have lots of company." I paused momentarily for emphasis, then continued: "and I do have the satisfaction of having *tried*!"

Cleve gave me the choice of an aircraft carrier or a position as senior medical officer of the Naval Air Station at Agana,

Guam. I chose Guam and had been on the island nearly 12 months when the twenty-fifth celebration of Guam Liberation Day was held.

As Jimi and I strolled through the fairgrounds, I thought about the last 12 months. The move had not been easy. I couldn't remember any easy moves. Danny was married and in the Army. Dewey and Diane had come to the island long enough to talk me into letting them finish high school at the Mid Pacific Institute, a boarding school in Hawaii. Jimi and I were settled in navy quarters on the Naval Air Station. The quarters could benevolently be called adequate, but they were worlds away from the large house on Point Lookout Drive. I was settled into my new job, and Jimi was teaching in an almost totally Guamanian school.

I tried the portable radio once more to see if there would be an announcement to let us know how the moon walk was progressing; there was none. Neil Armstrong and Buzz Aldrin were two men with whom I had worked closely for nearly five years. We had shared an important time in our lives. Now these two men were exploring the surface of the moon and sharing their excitement with the whole world—except us. Jimi and I were in one of the few parts of the inhabited world that did not have live television coverage of this historic event. Now, we did not even have radio coverage! Suddenly, we both felt totally isolated.

Some of this isolation had been felt soon after we landed on Guam. One of my responsibilities as the senior medical officer of NAS Agana and flight surgeon on the staff of the Commander of Naval Forces in the Marianas was to provide medical support to air evacuation flights to the Trust territory of the Pacific Islands. This group of over 2,000 islands had been under the control of the U.S. Navy after the war. They were transferred to the United Nations when that organization was formed, and in turn made the administrative responsibility of the U.S. Department of the Interior. Again, the Navy was asked to provide support.

During the first week after my arrival on Guam, an air evacuation mission had been requested to transport a sick girl from the island of Woolei. I needed flight time, so I donned my flight suit and met the rest of the crew in operations. We had soon landed in a large lagoon and were receiving taxi instructions from a native in a bright red loincloth called a *theu*. The anchor was dropped close to the beach. Almost immediately, an outrigger canoe was alongside. After a semidry landing (which meant that my medical bag did not go completely underwater), I was following the red theu across the island at a half run. I had seen the island from the air and knew it was a narrow spit of land not more than 1/2 mile long; it seemed much larger once I was on the ground.

Finally, we arrived at a large grass hut and I was ushered inside. As my eyes adjusted to the dim light, I realized why we had seen only men on the beach. All the women on the island were crowded into this one hut with the patient in the center. When my eyes were more accustomed to the dark interior, I could see that the patient was the only female in the room who was dressed in anything more than the traditional grass skirt. This could have been Hawaii 200 years ago! I pretended not to notice the hundred bare torsos in the room and went to work in center stage under the watchful eye of a large gecho (lizard) who was perched on the thatched ceiling observing my every move.

The patient was a 13-year-old girl who had periods of unconsciousness. There were no physical findings except the apparent lethargy. I felt intimidated by the lack of laboratory data and the lack of sophisticated medical equipment. I even felt intimidated by the gecho. What did he expect me to do? Perhaps I should rattle some bones or at least burn some incense. Instead, I said a few medical words and decided to take her back to Guam.

It was some consolation that, after the doctors at the U.S. Naval Hospital in Guam ran a battery of laboratory tests and used their sophisticated medical equipment, they could not make a clinical diagnosis either. Her anxious father had accompanied the patient to Guam and caused quite a commotion with the charge nurse when he insisted on pacing outside the hospital room clad only in his bright red theu.

For the last 10 years, I had been totally involved in high-performance jet aviation and in the nation's space program. Now, it was as though by some warp of time I was transported back 200 years. Even the island of Guam had been a cultural shock, but Woolei? Nukuoro? Kapingamaringi? Most of the inhabitants had never seen an aircraft of any kind. They knew of nothing that didn't exist on their tiny island. How fortunate I was to have been exposed to this primitive way of life before it totally disappeared. The natives went about their utopian routine, as they had for generations, savoring one beautiful sunset after another. They were innocently unaware of the larger, bustling world around them.

On the tiny island of Kapingamaringi, bright-eyed Polynesian children were trying to teach me their language even before I had secured the stern line of the HU16 to a nearby coconut tree. Their way of life would undoubtedly change simply because I had been there. Was there a way that the peace and contentment of this primitive existence could be preserved while they were introduced to the benefits of a space-age society? It had not happened in any culture I had visited or read about, but these children were special. Perhaps . . .

———————

I had been ordered to active duty involving "flying on operational and training flights as a naval aviator," and although the HU16 Albatross did not fly like an A-4 Skyhawk, I finally managed to master it. I particularly enjoyed the water operations; this was a different type of flying than I had ever been exposed to. It was difficult to believe that you could slow a multiengine plane down to 70 knots and still be airborne. I was used to landing at nearly twice that speed. The Albatross was an amphibious aircraft; it could operate off the water or land. Water landings were the most fun, but conventional landings on a runway could be interesting. I soon found that my carrier approach did not work. If I landed the Albatross like I was used to landing the Skyhawk, it would promptly bounce 20 feet in the air. Finally, I almost got the knack of it and flew air evacuation missions every time I had a chance. I was thoroughly enjoying my assignment on Guam.

Unfortunately, Jimi did not share my excitement. Teaching in a Guamanian school was an experience, but not always an enjoyable one. It did not help for our shipment of household effects to have been delayed five months, then arrive during a rainstorm that proceded one of the typhoons that seemed to roar across the island every weekend. The movers were unrolling her queensized mattress on the wet ground when Jimi arrived home from school. The sight of her long-anticipated mattress was bad enough; I hesitated to show her the crate in which her treasured oil paintings had arrived.

It had caused quite a scene in Houston when she insisted on wooden crates for her good oil paintings rather than the cardboard ones the packers wanted to use. She persisted and prevailed, but someone, somewhere along the tortuous journey, had managed to put two prongs of a forklift directly through the crate from a broadside. This was one broadside too many, and I was visibly worried about her reaction to this latest catastrophe.

I need not have worried. This petite southern belle could handle it. In her typically gracious manner, Jimmieline, who usually didn't drink, poured herself a water glass full of triple sec and passed out on the queensized bed.

The complete isolation of Guam was broken occasionally by the visit of an old friend. Gene and Barbara Cernan accompanied Vice President Spiro Agnew on a visit to the island, and Jimi and Barb were able to spend an afternoon together. When Neil Armstrong accompanied the Bob Hope USO Show to Guam, Neil invited us to the party given by the Air Force general at Anderson Air Force Base. We were able to meet Bob Hope and his entire troupe, including Lola Falana, Connie Stevens, Les Brown, and Miss Universe. Jimi had her picture taken with Less Brown and talked with Bob Hope. This was more excitement than she had experienced since she arrived on the island.

Miss Universe was a fragile beauty from Sweden, and when I noticed that she had a pair of USAF wings pinned to her lace gown, I felt obligated to pin a shining set of gold Navy wings directly above them. I knew I was then out of uniform at a function given by an Air Force general, but she was so lovely I would have given her anything she wanted.

Aside from these bursts of excitement, the move was not working for Jimi. I had my friends, my work, my flights to the Trust Territory, diving, and golf. As a flight surgeon, I could make official trips to Japan, Hong Kong, Okinawa, Viet Nam, Thailand, and even Hawaii. Jimi was stuck with a roomful of Guamanian school kids who had never seen a train, and who would not have anything to do with their classmate because he was a Japanese, a Palauan, a Trukese, or worst of all, a Statesider. She was learning that the South did not have a corner on the market when it came to discrimination.

She had also learned not to try to stop a fight between a Guamanian and a native from the island of Palau. Palau was a beautiful island 700 miles south of Guam that I had visited several times. The native Palauans were a proud race and had an island tradition of protecting personal territory. They could be fierce competitors and were known to use large stones to make their point in an argument. I had noticed that most of our air evac trips to Palau were to transport a head injury to the U.S. Naval Hospital on Guam. Most of the head injuries were caused by large stones thrown by other Palauans.

Luckily, the large stone had missed the Guamanian student and the teacher who had tried to intervene, but it did make Jimi wonder if she was cut out for this sort of life. The turning point probably came on her 40th birthday; that was the morning that a single Datsun hit a single power pole and knocked out the electricity on the entire island. Jimi was without the benefit of a bath or any of the other things she liked to do in the morning. Because it was her birthday, a fellow teacher had presented her with a present that should have raised her spirits. She did appreciate the thought until she opened the package and found an orange sweatshirt with big, black lettering, **GUAM IS GOOD**.

Our marriage wasn't working either. The quick transition from a full house to an empty nest in one giant step could have been a contributing factor, but there there were so many other factors. Jimi felt isolated—stagnated. She was disinterested in her work, her environment, her husband, her marriage; nothing mattered. She needed a change.

When Jimi decided to quit her teaching job after the first year and leave the island, I didn't object. We would make the final decision and settlement later, but for now, I would vacate our quarters, store the household effects, and move into the bachelor officers' quarters. I would accompany Jimi to Manila where she would launch into an extended trip to visit Thailand, Vietnam, Laos, Cambodia, Indonesia, and Hong Kong. She had friends in most of these places, but mainly she planned to see what she wanted to do with her life. Although the term *find yourself* would not become popular for another decade, it was entirely appropriate for the situation.

The trip was not a spur-of-the-moment affair. She had corresponded with Jiggs and Pat Weldon, who had both been in my medical school class at LSU. Jiggs had been a Marine officer and had led his men on the first wave of the Third Division during the liberation of Guam. They were now in Laos with the USAID group. I wondered if Jiggs had ever successfully made the transition from Marine officer to medical doctor.

Jimi had also corresponded with Dr. and Mrs. Sudeao in Indonesia. Dr. Sudeao was a thoracic surgeon and a general in the Indonesian Army. They had visited the Johnson Space Center, and Alan Bean had been asked to entertain the general and his wife. Alan asked us to help because the general was also a physician; it turned out to be a thoroughly delightful experience. As in many developing countries, in Indonesia physicians were among the most educated leaders and were sometimes asked to assume line commands. General Sudeao's last command had been as Chief of Staff of the entire Indonesian Army. Jimi was to find out much more about this fascinating couple when she accepted their invitation to visit them in Indonesia.

The parting in Manila was not without tears, but I, too, had to find myself. When Jimi left on the Pan American flight to Hong Kong. I took a military flight back to Guam and to my new home in the bachelor officers' quarters.

| 15 |

The Second Step

Jimi smiled at the waitress as she set the bottle of champagne on the table. "How did you know it was our twenty-fifth wedding anniversary?"

The pretty Yap Island girl's eyes revealed her secret with a quick glance at me. She could speak whole sentences with a twinkle of her eye or a raised eyebrow. This was the universal language of the Pacific islands that I had learned to read during my two years on Guam.

The small hotel dining room was furnished with several rows of oilcloth-covered wooden tables and an assortment of straight-backed chairs. This was the best and only hotel on Yap, and we were the only guests. The small fan in the corner stirred the hot, humid air, but did little for comfort. Both of our shirts were wet; we were anxious to get into diving gear and to the relative comfort of the water.

"May we put it in the refrigerator? My husband doesn't drink, but I'll enjoy it tonight."

We had celebrated our Silver Anniversary with a large party at the officer's club before leaving Hawaii, where I had been stationed for two years. Most of our friends thought we had the party early because we might not stay married until the sixth of June; we actually wanted to celebrate the date in private and have the time alone—together. I looked at my bride of twenty-five years. She was a different Jimmielene Black Kelly from the one I had known when we parted in Manila three years before. She was now a scuba diver, a private pilot, and a travel agent who had traveled to places in the world that I had only read about.

I surprised her with a question. "Why did you come back?"

She looked into my eyes and knew she didn't have to answer, but she would. "Oh, I needed to protect my investment." Then, with her own brand of island English showing in her eyes, she turned the query around. She wanted to see how I would answer such a direct question.

I thought back over the last three years. Both of us had had time to reevaluate our personal lives. We had both gained the confidence that we could live full and satisfying lives alone. The children were essentially grown. There was enough financial security; so that would not force us to stay married. Our marriage vows were still considered sacred, but this alone would not do it. There was really nothing to keep us together—except our love. I smiled and answered the question, "I had some investments to protect, too." We both laughed and headed for the beach.

We had left Hawaii one week before on a military flight to Guam and had taken Air Micronesia 500 miles south to Yap. We would spend some time on Palau, then return to Hawaii by way of Guam, Truk, and Ponope. Scuba diving in Palau was some of the best I had seen in over twenty years of diving. Although this was Jimi's first real diving trip, I wanted it to be a memorable one. I wanted to show Jimi the underwater cave in Palau that Dewey and I had discovered and explored two years before. I wanted to take her on dives in Truk lagoon where most of the Japanese fleet had been sunk by carrier-based dive bombers during the war in the Pacific. I wanted Jimi to see some of the Pacific that she had missed from a Guamanian school room—the part that I had become so infatuated with.

My position as senior medical officer at the Naval Air Station in Barber's Point, Hawaii, had kept me busy since my arrival in the summer of 1970. This was particularly true because the position included additional duties as deputy director of the Naval Regional Medical Center, Hawaii, and staff flight surgeon for Admiral Thomas Hayward, commander of Fleet Air Hawaii. Even with this busy schedule, I still found some time to fly the A-4 Skyhawks based at the naval air station.

Our present quarters were not as large as the house in Nassau Bay, but the location more than made up for the size. The house was on the beach with a clear view of spectacular sunrises over Diamond Head and even more spectacular sunsets over Barber's Point. There were twenty-three coconut palms on the grounds, and I had learned to wield a machete like a native. Even when the entire medical department came over for a party, I could find enough coconuts and carve them so fifty guests could sip Jimi's special drink directly from the coconut shells.

Jimi had begun working with a travel agency in the local community of Eva Beach. The new job was a natural for her. She had a gift for remembering vivid details of every place she had visited, and she seldom had to route a client to a destination she had not personally visited. The little Louisiana girl who had hardly been out of Natchitoches Parish before we were married had now traveled in nearly 100 counties and had clearly outdistanced my travels. During the first years of our marriage, I had been the one who was away all of the time while she stayed home with the kids. Now, I was the one who couldn't get away except to take her to the airport and meet her arriving flights.

NASA's second step seemed to be working well, too. After the near disaster on *Apollo 13* that I had read about in a two-month old *Newsweek*, the moon exploration was going well. *Apollo 15* was scheduled to land just off Hawaii and would be greeted by the area commander, Admiral Thomas Hayward, accompanied by his staff flight surgeon.

When the admiral's party arrived on the U.S.S. *Okinawa*, I met many of my old friends who were deployed for the postlanding medical examinations. Drs. Clarence Jernigan, Bill Carpenter, and Wyck Hoffler were aboard to provide medical support to the mission, and Dr. Carter Alexander was the physiologist who would conduct the post-flight exercise test and act as the ground-based control for these studies. They welcomed me into the examination area, and after viewing my first splashdown of a spacecraft, I accompanied the NASA medical personnel to the examination room.

Astronaut Dave Scott was nearly seated on the bicycle ergometer when he looked up and saw the flight surgeon who was preparing to monitor the test. The trick had worked—Dave was thoroughly confused. "Fred! What are you doing here?"

I looked at my good friend who had just returned from a walk on the moon and replied, "Well, Dave, Admiral Hayward said that if you are going to land in his ocean, his flight surgeon would just have to check you out."

The reunion was fun, but the checkout was more than either of us bargained for. There was definitely some deterioration in Dave's performance compared to his pre-flight test and his ground-based control. This was the first time that Carter had outperformed Dave in an exercise test.

When Jim Irvine began his test, we were worried. Each time the computer put a load on the ergometer, the astronaut who had just walked on the moon would nearly pass out. The test was discontinued. I knew that the shock of unexpectedly seeing an old friend would not cause this type of reaction. The answer came after blood tests were back, confirming an electrolyte imbalance with potassium deficiency, apparently caused by electrolyte losses during the moon walk that had not been replaced. They needed to drink more orange juice. I later understood that this simple correction had worked on subsequent flights.

By the time Admiral Hayward hosted the formal dinner that night, his guests of honor were recovered. In retrospect, the Crew Flight Surgeon, Dr. Clarence Jernigan, thought that this exercise test might have been the earliest indication of incipient coronary artery disease that would cause Astronaut Jim Irvine to have a heart attack after he left NASA.

The *Apollo 15* recovery was a good time to visit old friends and catch up on all the latest at JSC. Dr. Bill Carpenter was a Canadian who had stayed at JSC when Nig Coons and I left. He had served as crew flight surgeon on the first moon landing and had experienced the elaborate quarantine measures with the crew. There had been some worry about the possibility that the Apollo crew would contact some wild, exotic moon microbe to which earthlings had developed no immunity. This possibility was not as wild as it may sound. Anyone familiar with early Hawaiian history will remember what measles did to the local population when it was first introduced.

Dr. Clarence Jernigan had served as the Recovery Area Quarantine Manager on the first moon landing, and reported that no life, exotic or otherwise, was found; so there were no quarantine measures on *Apollo 15*. Clarence had completed his specialty training in aerospace medicine shortly before I left NASA and had become an important member of the medical team. Bill Carpenter had completed training in nuclear medicine. He was performing some tests on the *Apollo 15* crew that I understood about as well as I understood orbital mechanics. Wyck Hoffler was a bright young internist from North Carolina who had joined NASA's staff about the time I left.

Of the NASA friends aboard the *Okinawa* for this recov-

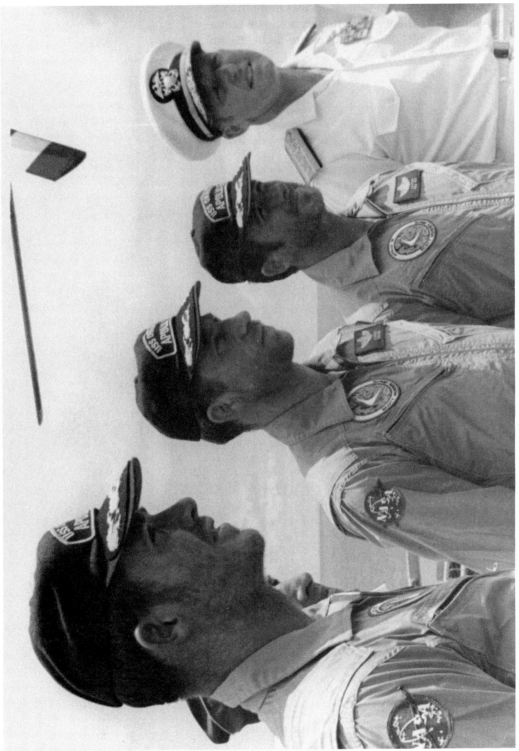

The Apollo 15 astronauts—from left to right, Dave Scott, Al Worden, and Jim Irwin—are welcomed aboard the U.S.S. Okinawa by Admiral Tom Hayward. The astronauts' performances in their post-flight exercise tests were less than expected due to dehydration and a possible electrolyte imbalance. Admiral Hayward was commander of Fleet Air Hawaii and in charge of the Navy recovery forces in the Pacific at this time. He was later chief of Naval Operations. (Courtesy NASA)

ery, Carter Alexander was the biggest surprise. I remembered him as a pudgy young physiologist who had managed to get NASA funding for additional training in aerospace physiology. Carter had completed this training after I left Houston, was now a Ph.D. in physiology, and had completely changed his image. He looked taller, but this was probably an illusion; he was lean and more muscular from his acquired habit of running five miles a day. A beard and a Florida tan completed the transformation. I remembered the name well, but the man was different.

From my NASA friends, I was able to find out how the latest reorganization of Medical Operations was (or wasn't) working; who had left the program; and who had been divorced. The newly selected medical astronauts had no chance of flying on Apollo, and perhaps one of them, Joe Kerwin, would fly on Skylab. The other scientist astronauts were not faring much better. One of their number had already become disillusioned and quit to resume a teaching career.

I was able to add bits of news. Jimi and I had met Wally Schirra in the lobby of the Waikiki Sheraton. He was into real estate and working on some deal in Princeville on the north shore of Kauai. We had laughed because we had, also, looked at lots in Princeville. The salesman had said, "Astronaut Schirra has the lot right over there." On our way to Hawaii we had looked at lots in Crested Butte, Colorado, and the salesman had said, "Astronaut Schirra has the lot right over there." Wally was really getting around in the real estate field since he left NASA.

I had also seen Scott Carpenter at a diving symposium in Honolulu. He and Rene had divorced some time ago. After we talked a few minutes, Scott had excused himself to meet his son. From the worried look on his face, I knew that all of his family problems had not been completely resolved.

Other than these bits of information, I had been effectively isolated from my former life at NASA. I could report that the Navy had been good to me, and I had received my fourth stripe as a Navy captain shortly after returning to active duty. My Navy career was progressing well. Admiral Frank Voris, who was also a naval aviator/flight surgeon, had engineered my transfer from Guam to Barber's Point, Hawaii, because of problems at the Barber's Point Medical Department. I had been able to clean up the old wooden buildings and brighten up the services. I had also been able to make some recommendations to BUMED. As a result, the department scrapped the approved plans for a new dispensary and funded an expanded clinic using many of my recommendations.

Admiral Tom Hayward had written a fitness report that was so good it was almost embarrassing. He recommended me for an early promotion to the rank of rear admiral. Admiral Frank Voris was going to be on the promotion board. However, I knew that, even with the cards stacked so heavily in my favor and with a personal recommendation from a Line Admiral who was clearly on his way to greater things (Admiral Hayward was later chief of Naval Operations), the chances of a reserve flight surgeon making flag rank were nil.

This was confirmed when I found that another member of the board was the senior medical officer I had crossed swords with at Cecil Field. I had rocked the boat once too often and would not get the broad stripe.

| 16 |

Spaceport USA

Duane Graveline and I watched from the roof of the clinic at Kennedy Space Center, on April 12, 1981, as the first shuttle lifted off, leaving a trail of dense, white smoke. Jimi had a much better view from the VIP stands near the Launch Control Center.

It was not as though we had never witnessed the launch of a spacecraft before. I had seen Mercury, Gemini, and Apollo launches, and many unmanned launches. I did not expect to be affected by this launch—I was wrong. The sight was so spectacular, and the excitement in the air so electrifying, it was impossible to remain unaffected. It was good to see so much pride in an accomplishment. It was a national pride; it was contagious. The excitement was almost overwhelming. I half expected to see small American flags and marching bands. Around us, spontaneous cheers were erupting: *"Go! Go! Go! Go! Go! John, Go!"*

Duane and I watched silently, savoring this moment of vicarious achievement; we didn't begrudge the two men in the cockpit. Envy? Yes! John Young had flown five times, and I had been somewhere in the supporting cast for three of these flights. Supporting cast, hell! I wanted to fly! I looked at my friend of over twenty years. Duane Graveline had gotten much closer to his goal than I had; he was actually chosen as an as-

tronaut and was on his way when his wife delivered that broadside.

I was still using Navy terms even though I had retired from the Navy seven years ago. Jimi and I had traveled for nearly eighteen months before I took the job as medical director at NASA's Langley Research Center. Now I held the same position at Kennedy Space Center.

I remembered the events of fifteen years ago. Astronauts were supposed to be immune from social and martial ills. They were all fair-haired boys living in vine-covered cottages in perfect marital harmony. Duane's wife called a press conference to deliver an indictment so devastating that NASA had asked for his resignation. It was more than a request; he was out! Here was a man I considered head and shoulders above all the other scientist astronaut selectees. He was wasted because his wife had filed for divorce. If this was going to set a precedent, they would have to select more astronauts. Many of the present group were not living in perfect marital harmony, including the man who had just been launched on his fifth mission.

I had asked Duane to leave his busy family practice in Vermont and come to Florida for the first shuttle launch to help evaluate the disaster plans at Kennedy Space Center. I was only able to pay a token consultant fee that wouldn't even take care of expenses, but Duane had eagerly accepted the offer. Duane had remained active in the Vermont National Guard and flew helicopters on weekend drills when he could get away from his busy medical practice. It was good to have someone so well qualified to back up the paramedics if an emergency occurred and we needed to use the two NASA helicopters that were standing by at the clinic.

The potential for disaster is always great at a launch complex, but the *Columbia* was generations more complicated than any vehicle we had ever launched. The two large, solid rockets were of particular concern. Once they were ignited, there was no chance of shutting them down and certainly no chance of holding them on the pad. If they didn't fire absolutely simultaneously and continue firing with equal thrust, the shuttle could conceivably become a giant pinwheel. If this happened, the fireworks display could be spectacular and horrifying.

The *Columbia* had ejection seats, but an off-the-pad ejection was out of the question. NASA flight surgeons from JSC, with Department of Defense helicopters, were present to take care of the crew in case of an emergency. I had responsibility

Astronauts John Young and Bob Crippen begin a new era of spaceflight aboard the Space Shuttle Columbia on April 12, 1981. The excitement of success is still evident—almost overwhelming. It's good to see this much national pride in an accomplishment. (Courtesy NASA)

153

for the ninety thousand support personnel, VIPs, and other visitors. I had nightmares of the pinwheel landing on the NASA causeway among forty thousand spectators. We had been assured by the experts that this would not happen, but that didn't stop the nightmares. I remembered the expert's opinion that said Nig and I had overstated our concern for a fire hazard in Apollo.

Duane and I had driven from my condominium on Cocoa Beach to the space center shortly after midnight, and the traffic had already started. A trip that usually takes thirty minutes took nearly two hours. This gave Duane his first recommendation for his disaster critique: helicopter transportation is the only mode of emergency transportation you can count on during a launch.

The problem was not only the ninety thousand people who had gate passes to view the launch from Kennedy Space Center or Cape Canaveral Air Force Station. Many more viewers crowded the roads in the surrounding towns of Titusville, Cape Canaveral, Cocoa, Cocoa Beach, and as far south as Melbourne. The nearest hospital was fourteen miles away in Titusville. There were also hospitals in Cape Caneveral, Cocoa, Melbourne, and the U.S.A.F. Hospital at Patrick Air Force Base. NASA had designated the teaching hospital at Gainesville as the Definitive Medical Care Facility; the hospital's emergency helicopter with a team of emergency care physicians would be on hand for subsequent launches.

Since December of 1980, I had headed the Pan American World Service's contract with NASA to provide occupational medicine and environmental health support for Kennedy Space Center and Cape Canaveral Air Force Station. My staff, which numbered one hundred and twenty, included eight physicians, two Ph.D.s, and others with advanced degrees in everything from business administration to analytical chemistry and industrial hygiene. For this launch, in addition to the helicopter crews and the environmental health teams, I had deployed medical support teams to cover three clinics, the VIP viewing stands, the press site, and eight other locations where a significant medical requirement could be identified. In addition, the Navy Hospital in Orlando and the U.S.A.F. Hospital at Patrick each supplied two ambulance teams to support the launch.

Passes had also been issued to a number of visiting consultants from the local community so they would be available if needed. Even with this much professional help and with detailed plans reviewed from every viewpoint we could envision, I still had nightmares. The scope of the job could be overwhelming, but at least the first shuttle launch had gone without a hitch. The medical teams had reported only minor problems. None of my nightmares had materialized.

Duane and I followed the small assembled group down the iron ladder from the roof of the clinic and retreated to the relative quiet of my office. There was no need to rush. It would take hours for the visitors to leave the viewing sites so I could begin to recall the deployed medical personnel. We relaxed in my office with a cup of coffee and I spoke first. "Do you think we would have flown? I mean—if I had been selected and you had been able to stay in the program, do you think we would have flown a mission on Apollo or Skylab?"

Duane's answer was as I expected. "I would have sure given it a go."

"Yeah, I know you would, and I would have too. But what do you think our real chances would have been?"

Duane could answer that one without much serious thought. "Close to nil."

I had made my point, but I wanted to drive it home so Duane might find it easier to cope with some of the bitterness and disappointment that was showing in his eyes. "Look at it this way, Duane. You were head and shoulders above anyone else we had as far as scientific ability and accomplishments in space medicine research, but you were clearly oriented toward medicine. Who had more to say about who flew what mission than anyone else?"

Duane had no trouble answering that question either. "That's right, Deke Slayton. Who was John Young's patron saint? The same Donald K. Slayton, Chief of the Astronaut Corps. Now, who was the only medical astronaut to fly on Skylab?"

Duane saw the line of reasoning, and it made some sense. He was definitely oriented toward medical research and could not expect support from the Astronaut Office. The Medical Directorate had very little to say about crew selection, and Duane might even have been perceived as a threat to Chuck's position as Chief Medical Spokesman. Medical Astronaut Joe Kerwin figured this out early and positioned himself squarely in the Astronaut Office.

I continued, "Joe and I talked about this when he first came aboard. You were in flight training at Williams Air Force Base. Joe recognized the tension between Chuck Berry and Deke Slayton and didn't want to get caught in the crossfire. I think it would have been unavoidable for you or me. We could not have sat back and failed to pushed for a reasonable medical research program, not only because we represented and supported Chuck, but because it was right and urgently needed. This would have effectively alienated us from Deke and most

155

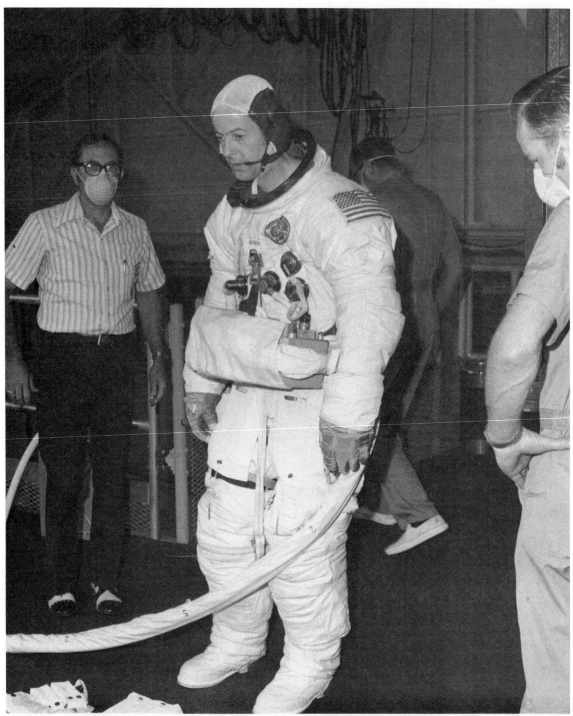

Dr. Joe Kerwin, a flight surgeon/naval aviator, is chosen as the first medical astronaut to fly in space. During Skylab 2, Astronauts Kerwin and Conrad performed a crucial EVA to deploy a damaged solar panel that would give them electrical power and make the Skylab habitable for subsequent flight crews. (Courtesy NASA).

156

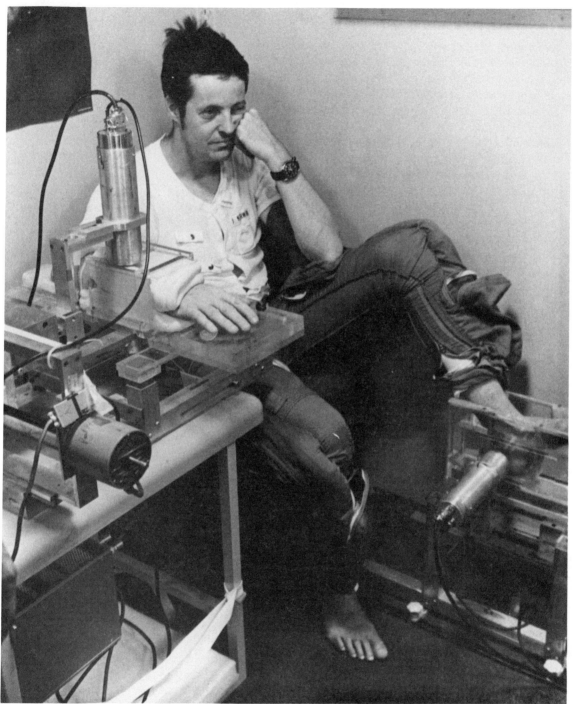

Commander Joseph P. Kerwin, Medical Corps, U.S. Navy, undergoes a post-flight medical scan for bone demineralization after his flight in Skylab 2. Although you wouldn't know it from this photograph, Joe remains indestructible. He is now director of Space and Life Sciences for NASA at the Johnson Space Center, Houston, Texas. (Courtesy NASA)

157

of the other astronauts. I think it would have been a cold day in hell before either of us were selected for a flight.''

Astronaut Joe Kerwin also watched the first shuttle launch. He added technical color for one of the major newscasters and handled the spotlight of national television very well. As well as adding technical items to the newscast, he added the personal warmth and the credibility of one who had actually been there.

He had certainly done a creditable job on his Skylab flight. The Skylab had been damaged during launch. When they arrived, temperatures in the Skylab were over 120 degrees Fahrenheit. The all-Navy crew was able to install a makeshift solar screen to replace the micrometeorite shield that had been lost during launch and get the temperature under control. Astronauts Kerwin and Conrad then performed a crucial EVA to deploy the damaged solar panel, giving them electrical power and making the Skylab habitable for subsequent crews. Joe had proven that a flight surgeon/naval aviator could be effective as an astronaut. I had never doubted this, but it was good to get confirmation and recognition for this particular breed of aeromedical specialist.

The traffic was finally thinning out and I could release all of my staff except the duty crew. We would have time to pick up Jimi and have a bite at Fat Boy's Barbecue before Duane had to catch his plane back to Vermont. On the way to the condominium, Duane asked how Jimi was taking our oldest son Danny's disappearance. ''Not too well, I'm afraid. It's on her mind most of the time.''

Danny had been divorced again and had started an artificial stone company in Houston. Jimi had visited him and was impressed by some of the fireplaces and decorative stone walls they had installed. When Danny came to Oregon in September of 1978 for our younger son Dewey's wedding, the business was going well. Several months later, I made a trip to Houston and was unable to find him at any of the addresses I had. The office and home telephone had been disconnected, and there was no trace of a forwarding address. Since then, Danny had called Dewey several times. He had moved to Mexico but left no address or telephone number. The last call had been over six months ago; there had been absolutely no contact since then. Danny had lapsed into periods of silence before, but nothing like this and never for this long. I tried to console Jimi with the usual, ''Don't worry, he can take of himself. After all, he is thirty-three years old.'' My efforts were not very convincing because I was worried, too.

Duane broke the silence by asking, ''Have you thought of getting in touch with the embassy or making a trip down there?''

I nodded. ''It would be like looking for a needle in a haystack, but if we don't get this contract renewed, I want to take some time and try. Dewey has some leads we could start with.''

The doubt about the contract caught Duane off guard. ''What do you mean, if you don't get this contract renewed? Pan Am has it locked up.''

I took my eyes off the road for a second, ''Duane, you haven't dealt with government contracts. It doesn't matter how good a job you've done or how dedicated and conscientious you and your staff are. You can still be shot out of the saddle by any joker who can lie, cheat, and steal better than you can. They don't have to be able to do the job. All they have to do is to say they can do it better and cheaper than you can. That's called buying in.''

I paused and continued, ''I'm at a disadvantage here because I know the scope of the job. I know what has to be done to have a good occupational medicine and environmental health program. I know the consequences of an incomplete program, and I haven't learned to lie, cheat, and steal very well yet. I still haven't learned to compromise. Besides that, Pan Am has had so much trouble with this dinkie little contract they may not even rebid it.''

We passed the small town of Cape Caneveral and were in Cocoa Beach. Florida Highway A1A became North Atlantic Boulevard, and on the left we could see the seventeen-story condominium on the beach. I waved at the guard as we turned into the red brick driveway and found a parking place.

After Duane's flight left, Jimi said she was worried about Duane. He was expecting too much of his second wife, and Jimi was afraid they were headed for marital troubles. The conversation went on to the number of our friends in the space program who had or were having problems in their marriages. I didn't keep up with such things, but Jimi could give you the score without even looking at the unfamiliar names in her address book.

''I don't know if you can blame all of that on the space program. Look at all of the new wives that keep showing up at my medical school reunions?'' The Class of '51 had just had its thirty-year reunion at the LSU School of Medicine in New Orleans. I had been able to attend every one so far and was amused to see the number of new wives that kept popping in—and out—of the reunions.

Jimi had her reply ready. "That just means you went to medical school with a bunch of dirty old men."

I expected this. She had used it before, but I didn't let it faze me. "Does it make any difference if these dirty old men are doctors, or astronauts, or maybe the host on a late-night television program? How many wives has Johnny Carson had?" Neither of us knew the answer to that question.

I had watched the "Johnny Carson Show" for years before Jack Tolar had pointed out "Kit Carson" in our 1945 "Bobashela" yearbook from Millsaps College was the same Johnny Carson who had made late-night television into an institution. The "definitely tricky Kit Carson" had been performing magic tricks when he was photographed for the yearbook. I remembered "Kit Carson" as just another nondescript apprentice seaman who managed to stay out of sight and didn't make waves. He was not nearly as flashy as Jack Tolar.

Jimi, also, would not be deterred from making her point. "I know there are problems in any group, but I think the problems faced by the first three or four groups of astronauts were unique, and the cost to their wives and families have not been appreciated."

I couldn't argue with that line of reasoning, but my thoughts turned to the shuttle program. I wondered if the next few years in the nation's space program was going to be any less demanding than the years of Mercury or Gemini. They intended to launch thirty shuttles a year! This place was going to turn into a real spaceport. How do you plan for thirty launches a year? How do you plan for medical support to thirty launches a year?

I remembered this conversation several months later when we saw the *Challenger* for the first time. The brand new shuttle was arriving at the Kennedy Space Center Shuttle Landing Facility, piggyback on NASA's 747. I had invited Jimi out to watch the arrival. It was quite an impressive sight as the pilot made a low pass over the field before the landing. After it was parked near the mate-demate device, a familiar figure stepped down from the 747 and walked into operations. Jimi had been escorted to the visitor's section, and I was checking with my ambulance crews. As soon as I could excuse myself, I followed the group into operations.

"Joe Algranti, I thought you were a helicopter pilot. I didn't know you could fly these big birds." After the initial surprise and greetings, Joe said the 747 handled like a big baby, even with the *Challenger* on its back. The conversation soon turned to talk about Joe's ejection from the lunar trainer.

The Space Shuttle Columbia returns piggyback to the Kennedy Space Center aboard NASA's specially configured Boeing 747—ready to fly again. (Courtesy NASA)

"Yeah, that was a close one. A few more seconds and I would have been inverted." Joe had been flying a test hop on the lunar excursion module trainer when a malfunction caused it to roll. He ejected at the last instant before the craft rolled over and disappeared in a large fireball. Joe was still indestructible!

I was able to retrieve a hot and tired Jimmielene from behind the ropes, and we completed a quick visit with Joe before he was called to a meeting. It would take most of the night to demate the *Challenger* from the 747, drop the landing gear, and tow it to the Orbiter Processing Facility. This was the first time that two shuttles would be in the facility at the same time. When the *Columbia* arrived at the Cape for the first time, it was missing many of its protective tiles, but there was no evidence of that problem with the *Challenger*.

I thought, again, of the magnitude of the support problems. Thirty launches a year! Even the problems ahead for the small medical support contract were staggering. Each shuttle would be landed at this strip, towed to the Orbiter Processing Facility, mated to the external tank and solid rocket boosters in the vertical assembly building, transported on the crawler to the pad, and launched. Each step of this operation would be followed closely by members of the Occupational Medicine and Environmental Health Team. We had to provide close medical support for each hazardous operation. In this business, there were very few operations which were not hazardous.

Environmental Health's task was to detect toxic gases, check for breathable atmospheres, protect against radiation hazards, and work with the Shuttle Processing Contractor at each stage of the operation to help protect the health of the workers. We must also be concerned with the thousands of VIPs and other visitors who are attracted to this area.

Thirty shuttle launches a year! How do you plan for medical support for thirty launches a year? I was beginning to sound like a broken record. While we watched the *Challenger* being lifted from the larger aircraft, Jimi noticed the slight grimace on my face and read my thoughts. "Cheer up! It may not be your problem." I was always amused that she could display such a grasp of almost any situation. I was also amazed that she seemed to know exactly what I was thinking about at almost any moment.

"You'll have to admit, the next ten years at Kennedy Space Center are going to be interesting. I really do hope I'm around to see it."

Jimi wasn't so sure she could share my hopes. The past year had been interesting. It had also been unbelievably demanding. My staff was smaller than other groups I had managed effectively, but I had never faced such an array of demanding administrative problems before in my entire career. There were times when Jimi felt closed out of my world. She had partially understood several months before when I had come home from some particularly trying union negotiations. I had sat down heavily on the bed and said "It isn't that I don't want to talk to you about it. I just don't want to *talk*."

In the small Occupational Medicine and Environmental Health Contract that Pan American World Airways had held since 1971, there had been a succession of seven medical directors. To complicate matters, the staff belonged to two unions: the International Brotherhood of Teamsters and the Transportation Workers of America. There were four bargaining units, which included the clerical workers, the nurses, the environmental health and laboratory technicians, and the corpsmen and paramedics.

Even though the state of the art in emergency medical services had made remarkable advances in the last ten years, as medical director I was forced to work with bargaining agreements designed in the 1970s. I could not assign my most qualified personnel to the most crucial task. On any given ambulance run I might have a paramedic or a nurse with exceptional qualifications in emergency medicine, or I might have one who had not started an IV in twenty years. Jimi silently hoped that the next ten years would not be her husband's problem.

Now, it was I who could read her thoughts. A short time later, after we had taken all of the pictures of the *Challenger* we wanted and were on our way back to Cocoa Beach, I decided to bring the subject up again. "I know this job hasn't been any easier on you than it has on me, but it needs to be done right. If we are able to set the contract up right, it'll work, and everyone, even the Teamsters, will be happy with it. I really think we can pull it off."

Jimi's body English told me that the little Louisiana girl was not to be convinced; so I changed the subject. "You know that the first crew on the *Challenger* will include a physician? Yeah, Story Musgrove is getting a chance to fly. I think there are several other medical types in the program now."

I had met Jim and Ann Fisher at a Department of Defense briefing while they were here as flight surgeons in the Air Force rescue helicopters for the fourth mission. I had also seen these two physicians in a television interview, and was impressed

Dr. Anna L. Fisher, one of the 35 new astronauts selected on January 31, 1978, poses with her husband, Dr. William Fisher. After this photograph was taken, Dr. Bill Fisher was also selected as an astronaut. Spaceflight is, finally, operational, and aerospace medicine is being well represented. What a future they have! (Courtesy NASA)

at how well they were able to field the questions and project an image of competence to the TV audience. The fact that they were married to each other did not seem to be a factor in either career. In light of the history of marital problems in most of the astronauts and doctors I knew, I wondered what the tensions of the shuttle program would bring to their marriage.

I couldn't bring myself to feel too sorry for these two medical astronauts. What a future they had! They were both so young and so sure of where they were going. I could envy them, but there was no malicious envy or bitterness. I was satisfied with what I had accomplished. In spite of Cleve Hunley's remarks, I didn't feel like a loser. I just no longer felt indestructible. I considered myself extremely lucky to have been closely associated with each of the nation's manned space programs. I had received much more personally and professionally from that association than I had contributed.

I wondered about Jim and Ann Fisher. With thirty launches a year, there was no doubt that they would fly and fly again. They were entering into a new era, and their potential really was unlimited.

Yes, I envied them.

|17|

Reflections

The sunset on the Red Sea was spectacular! When we reached the beach that afternoon in April, 1983, the sea was a deep azure; however, as the sun began to set, a magical transformation began. The sand, the sea, and the sky were blending into a rich, burnt orange that vibrated in our senses. At sunset the Red Sea was actually red—the scene was breathtaking.

The next morning my first dive in the Red Sea presented an ever-changing underwater panorama of bright coral and active sea life. The Red Sea had earned its reputation as one of the world's great diving spots. In my personal dive book, the underwater scenery there had to be rated as high as other great dives I had made at Bonair, at Palau, in the Truk Lagoon, and on Australia's Great Barrier Reef.

I had expected the underwater scenery in the Red Sea to be spectacular, but I was not prepared to see anything but miles upon miles of desert sands in the Kingdom of Saudi Arabia. I was in for a pleasant surprise. The four-hour drive from Tabuk to the Red Sea had carried members of the scuba diving club through some of the most interesting rock formations I had seen in my years of traveling. I needed more time to become familiar with this fascinating land. One of the reasons I had accepted a temporary assignment as flight surgeon for the

Royal Saudi Air Force was to see if I would like to return for a more permanent position. Now I was hooked; I could spend years exploring the many facets of this interesting country.

The two months passed quickly, and I found myself busily making arrangements to return home. I had two very important reasons to travel directly to our condominium at Cocoa Beach, Florida: to meet Jimi in time for our thirty-fifth wedding anniversary and to attend the forty-year reunion of my high school graduation class. It was difficult for me to believe that enough time had passed to make either of these events possible.

They say you can never go back; yet I *had* returned to the same land that I had visited first in 1955. Then I was a flight surgeon for the U.S. Navy transport squadron; now, I was a flight surgeon for a Saudi Air Force jet fighter squadron. One of the Saudi pilots had remarked, ''That was a different Saudi Arabia.'' The young lieutenant had made another observation that was equally astute, if not entirely appreciated at the time; ''I had not even been born when you first visited my country.''

I had thoroughly enjoyed my visit to this distant past. I had developed a good rapport with the squadron pilots and other flight personnel. I had won the support and personal friendship of General Hamdan, the commanding general of the air base. I had all of the ingredients needed to be effective as a flight surgeon. I could supply the competence and integrity.

It was good to be a real flight surgeon again.

In her last letter Jimi had included some assorted news clippings, the latest news about Duane Graveline, and a *Newsweek* article on John Glenn. She was excited about the possibility of living in Saudi Arabia; this was one of the few places in the world that she had never been able to visit. She, also, wanted to dive in the Red Sea. If I did return, we planned to keep our condominium on Cocoa Beach, and she would spend part of her time there.

This may have been one of the reasons our marriage had survived thirty-five years while so many of our friends had divorced, remarried, and divorced again. Too many of our close friends who had contributed so much to the nation's space exploration found it difficult to adjust to a new life after leaving NASA. I had recently read Buzz Aldrin's book that explained in some detail the problems he had encountered. He and Joan were divorced, and he was unable to resume his Air Force career because of alcoholism and mental illness. Buzz had easily contributed as much to the nation's space program as any other individual and had probably not received the full measure of credit he was due, even while he was making his contributions. After he left NASA, he must have found it difficult to join the ranks of the unknown and forgotten.

Someone had said that "nothing is as useless as yesterday's newspaper." You can use it to train the dog or wrap the rest of today's garbage in, but it's not useful for much else. That is true even if you were in the headlines. Jimi had found another use for old newspapers since I had been in Saudi Arabia. She clipped interesting articles and included one with nearly every letter.

I glanced at the *Newsweek* article that Jimi had sent in her last letter. There were John and Annie Glenn, smiling broadly, having just announced John's candidacy for the office of the President of the United States. They had made the post-NASA transition well.

I remembered the first year at Clear Lake when Jimi and I had season football tickets to all the high school football games; our seats were next to John's and Annie's. There were rare occasions when all four of us were there at the same time and could enjoy the game together, but more likely than not, John or I was away on NASA business, and the girls enjoyed the game and each other's company. Annie was a remarkable woman and had grown with John in his career.

The article credited her as being the "warmest and most genuine woman in politics. Having fought, and largely won, a life-long battle against a stutter, she brings a personal touch to Glenn's stiff military style." She would definitely be an asset in his campaign, as she had been during his entire career.

John looked older but still robust and healthy. He never did have the heart attack we had simulated to "fool the flight surgeons" at Langley. Jimi and I had talked to John and Annie at a party just before the Apollo-Soyuz launch; John was just as enthusiastic about his political career as he had been as an astronaut. As the article said, he was "a certifiable national hero, the sort of person Ronald Reagan might have played during his movie career. His combat record as a marine pilot— five distinguished flying crosses, eighteen air medals and twenty MiGs shot down in Korea—makes the Kennedy PT-109 look like dilettante boasting."

I remembered that John had only claimed three MiGs in Korea; so I was sure the article had not been cleared by the candidate. John had always been genuine. Of the first seven astronauts, he was the only one who met, and had his picture taken with, all of the aeromedical flight controllers at Langley in 1959. John was a politician even then. It didn't matter than, as Chuck Yeager said, he had to "brush the monkey chips off the seat" before he flew *Friendship 7*; he, like Enos, was a cut above all the other monkeys in the jungle.

Frank Borman was a "cut above" too. One of the clippings that Jimi had sent told how Frank, as president of Eastern Airlines, was having problems trying to keep the airline solvent in these troubled economic times. His management of the problems had been remarkable so far, but it looked like his most trying times were ahead. It was interesting to notice that most of the astronauts whom we thought were truly outstanding had distinguished themselves in other professions after leaving the space program. Maybe some of them were indestructible!

I looked back at the *Newsweek* article. "The Glenn's two children are, also, obvious assets: David, 37, is an anesthesiologist in San Francisco and Caroline Glenn Freeman is a doctor's wife in Vail, Colorado."

John also had his picture taken with my sons, Danny and Dewey Kelly, in front of the Space Task Group building at Langley. That picture was the envy of every kid on their block when the first American was orbiting the Earth.

David Glenn had been two years ahead of Danny in high school and had graduated before Danny's grades began to drop. Was that enough time to escape whatever happened to most of the teenagers in Nassau Bay and El Lago?

I folded the articles slowly and put them away while my thoughts went back to Danny. Why hadn't Danny at least let us know where he was? There must have been some reason, some event that had happened, some accident. I knew, intellectually, there was nothing to be gained by dwelling on this dark question, but I also knew the thought would never be far from my consciousness.

———

My mind wandered back over the last forty years. I had finished high school with my sights set squarely on the sky and beyond. I had reached more of my goals than I had any reason to expect, but was I indestructible? No, I had been destroyed many times; I had survived, but I couldn't claim indestructibility.

Ted Freeman had proven that the word had no place in

NASA's vocabulary. He had done everything right—seconds too late. Charlie Bassett and Elliott See—were they indestructible? C. C. Williams, another simple cross-country flight at 3,800 feet, and he hit the ground before he had time to eject. Gus Grissom, Ed White, and Roger Chaffee—they had no chance.

What about the near misses that could have so easily gone either way: the *Gemini 6a* engine shutdown, the *Gemini 8* control problem, the *Gemini 13* emergency, or the ejections from the lunar trainer?

What about the hidden cost? What about the Martha Chaffees and the Buzz Aldrins? What about the Danny Kellys? Had they been casualties of the times, or were they victims of someone's all-consuming drive to achieve? Was it worth the cost?

Indestructible? That question could be answered by a chorus of voices, No one is indestructible! But what of this illusion of indestructibility? Had it served any useful purpose? Had it allowed a "few to go where no man had gone before?"

Nearly forty years earlier I had learned to fly in an open-cockpit biplane. Along with most of my friends, I believed I was indestructible. Now some of my new friends were flying the space shuttles and planning permanent space stations! How much of this progress would have been possible if the fear of failure or death had been a dominating concern?

Would John Glenn have volunteered for his orbital mission if he had not been confident that it would be successful? What were his realistic odds of destroying three North Korean MiGs without himself being destroyed? He must have intellectually known these odds, but he continued and survived. Now he was reaching for the most responsible position in the free world with the same kind of confidence. The realistic odds were still against him, and he, again, must know these odds.

The President of the United States! Why would anyone want to assume such an awesome responsibility? Why did John Glenn want to be president of the United States? We could rule out the usual things such as fame, prestige, recognition—John had already ensured his rightful place in the history books. I knew that these items had never been high on John Glenn's priority list. No, John's decision to run for president must have been based on something more substantial and more in keeping with his character—possibly a sincere belief that he was better qualified for the position and could do the job better than any of the other candidates.

I had no trouble accepting this line of reasoning because I knew the man so much better than I could hope to know the other candidates. John Glenn would be an outstanding president. The qualities that made him outstanding as a Marine aviator and as an astronaut were the very qualities that I would like to see in the president of the United States.

I also knew that the most qualified candidate did not always win. John certainly shared this knowledge, but that would not keep him from pursuing his present challenge with his usual determination and confidence. John Glenn had always been ready to accept a new challenge, to reach farther toward the next goal, and to excel in each new quest.

What if he had stopped reaching for new goals after he became a Marine aviator? Few men have the ability and aptitude to become Marine aviators; he would undoubtedly have been considered an unqualified success by his peers.

John Glenn did not choose to stop and rest on his achievements. He became a war hero, then reached farther and became the first American to orbit the Earth. That was a singular accomplishment—no one else could ever hope to reach that goal—surely he could stop reaching then and claim permanent indestructibility.

But John Glenn still did not rest. He continued to accept new challenges and to pursue distant goals. He became a distinguished senator from Ohio and then reached for the highest goal in the free world. Is that what we mean by indestructibility?

I remembered what Joe Algranti had said about the T-38 pilots. "These are hot pilots; they need something with guts to challenge their skills and keep them sharp." Perhaps the challenge and the confidence that they can meet that challenge are the key ingredients needed to transform dreams into solid accomplishments.

The events of the last forty years had offered convincing proof that no one was indestructible. We must accept this fact, at least intellectually, as an overriding law of nature. It is equally true, however, that the progress over the last forty years could not have been made unless someone had been willing to accept the challenge, to ignore the fear of personal failure, and to secretly believe in the illusion of indestructibility.

Perhaps the concept of indestructibility cannot be decided by the success or failure of one great quest. The man or woman who has not failed has not tried hard enough—has not pushed to the limits of his or her capabilities and then reached farther with the same determination and confidence.

This belief of indestructibility has served us well. It has brought us from the open cockpit biplane to the space shuttle in forty short years. It has allowed us to walk on the surface of the moon. It has encouraged us to formulate plans for a permanent space station and to look beyond into futuristic space adventures that would have been science fiction a few years ago.

It seems appropriate that the first shuttle test vehicle had been named the *Enterprise*. This was the prototype of a magnificent fleet of spacecraft that would turn spaceflight into an operational reality and would allow a "few to go where no man had gone before."

Now that spaceflight is an operational reality, was it worth the cost? There are those who will argue that space exploration is a fiscal waste the country cannot afford. They sincerely believe that funds spent on space exploration could be better spent helping our own underprivileged and assisting underdeveloped countries with their financial needs. There are others who believe, just as sincerely, that a close, impartial examination will show the return from each dollar spent on space exploration more than justifies the cost in public funds.

What about the cost in lives?

> Astronaut Ted Freeman
> Astronaut Charlie Bassett
> Astronaut Elliott See
> Astronaut C. C. Williams
> Astronaut Gus Grissom
> Astronaut Ed White
> Astronaut Roger Chaffee

I had known each of these men personally and professionally. We were dedicated to the same cause. We dreamed the same dream. They recognized that their life might be taken at any turn, and they accepted the risk. To each of them, their dream was worth whatever risk was involved. Their spirit remains indestructible.

What of the hidden cost? The lives disrupted by death or by the living dedication—obsession—to a cause? What of the broken marriages? The sons and daughters whose lives were affected by someone's drive to achieve? The men and woman who failed to adjust to a new life after the space program?

Had my personal obsession caused Danny to alter his values and become lost in the jungle of life? Why hadn't the same obsession caused Dewey and Diane to lose their way? What about David Glenn? His dad had the same obsession, as well as the added complication of fame.

I put these questions to my son Dewey to get reflections from his generation of this turbulent period. He believes there is no tangible relation between these hidden costs and the space program. We could have been lawyers, politicians, business executives, or country doctors. We were dedicated to a cause, and those near to us were affected in one way or another. Some made the adjustment to life and others did not. Why? We may never know. There may not be a universal answer to such a question.

Dedication to a cause! Is that our culprit? Is dedication the two-edged sword that will carve our place in history—and wound the innocent? Must we, therefore, universally condemn ambition, dedication, or even obsession? Is it wrong to have a vision of a completed goal and the confidence that this goal can be achieved? Should we expose the illusion of indestructibility as a tragic farce?

Cold logic might suggest such a course, but I believe that to do so would condemn us to a life void of progress—a life in which individual and collective accomplishments would be nil and dreams would remain only dreams.

Dedication and the illusion of indestructibility have allowed brave men and women to walk close to the edge, have given them the commitment to success, and have brought us from the open-cockpit biplane to the reality of spaceflight. This progress has not been without cost, but those involved knew the risks and were able to accept these risks because of this same illusion.

The accomplishments in the last forty years have been due to the dedication, hard work, and personal sacrifice of many: Some who knew from the outset that no man is indestructible; some who learned this lesson from personal tragedy; and a few who, by fate or design, secretly managed to cling to this illusion.

The future belongs to those few.

Epilogue

While this book was being prepared for publication, tragedy again struck the nation's space program. Just 73 seconds after launch from Kennedy Space Center, the Space Shuttle *Challenger* and her crew of seven disappeared in a horrifying instant that left the world with the shocked realization that no one is indestructible.

We must now sadly add the names of seven more brave men and women to the list of those who accepted the risk and, through no fault of their own, were required to pay the price:

> Astronaut Francis R. "Dick" Scobee
> Astronaut Michael J. Smith
> Astronaut Ellison S. Onizuka
> Astronaut Judith A. Resnik
> Astronaut Ronald E. McNair
> Astronaut Gregory A. Jarvis
> Astronaut Christa McAuliffe

Five other names, unfamiliar to most readers, should also be added:

> Cosmonaut Valentin Bondarenko

who died in a fire when excessive oxygen was fed into his training chamber after the pressure was reduced. The accident, which was only revealed in April, 1986, occurred six years before the *Apollo 204* fire.

Cosmonaut Vladimir Komarov

who was killed April, 1967 when the Soyuz 1's parachute failed after reentry and the Russian spacecraft crashed.

Cosmonaut Georgi Dobrovolsky
Cosmonaut Vladislav Volkov
Cosmonaut Victor Patsayev

all of whom were killed in June 1971 when *Soyuz 11* experienced a loss of pressurization during reentry.

To these and to others who must certainly follow, I dedicate this book.

Astronaut Ronald McNair said it all before his death, "You can only become a winner if you are willing to walk over the edge."

Index

Edited by Suzanne L. Cheatle